The
YORKSHIRE
WEATHER
BOOK

The YORKSHIRE WEATHER BOOK

Bill Foggitt
& Len Markham

COUNTRYSIDE BOOKS
NEWBURY, BERKSHIRE

COUNTRYSIDE BOOKS
3 Catherine Road
Newbury, Berkshire

ISBN 1 85306 267 7

Front Cover: Pedal Eau – Lincoln Street, York, March 1968.
(Press Agency (York) Ltd)

Back Cover: A double-headed relief train on the Malton-Pickering line
delivers supplies to farms isolated by snow drifts in January 1958.
(Innis Studios, Hessle)

Designed by Mon Mohan

Produced through MRM Associates Ltd., Reading
Typeset by Paragon Typesetters, Queensferry, Clwyd
Printed in England

FOREWORD

The excesses of British weather have visibly shaped the Yorkshire landscape and its daily onslaughts have played no small part in moulding the stoical, pragmatic character of the Tyke. The British are world-renowned for their preoccupation with the weather, and we in Yorkshire in particular have good cause, when almost without regard to season, life is a constant battle with rain, wind, frost, snow and ice – and drought.

We have voiced our resigned indignation at our cantankerous climate since first we strode these broad acres, and begrudging tributes to Yorkshire weather often fleetingly appear in the media, and then are lost in newspaper archives, picture libraries and private collections. Now for the first time Yorkshire folk can recall all their yesterdays in this catalogue of mischief and memories of some very notable Yorkshire days.

This unique record is the result of close collaboration with Bill Foggitt, a well-loved figure in the annals of weather prediction. For generations, Bill's family has maintained weather journals, and careful record keeping and detailed observation of the natural world has enabled Bill for many years to predict with acclaimed success our climate's capricious moods. Extracts from his journals, and reminiscences which relate with humour his experiences of quirky Yorkshire weather have provided the sturdy backbone of the book. Join us as we wander through the centuries of climatic mayhem – but remember, we are relating only the worst Yorkshire can offer. A kindly sun still shines on a county filled with beauty!

Len Markham
July 1993

Pateley Bridge High Street, 1900. (Mrs F. Horner)

CONTENTS

Introduction	9
1. Yorkshire . . . Or what's left of it!	13
2. A Catalogue of Destruction	15
3. The Weather In The Early Years	20
4. The Nineteenth Century	24
5. The Twentieth Century	43
6. The Weather In The Thirties	48
7. The Weather In The Forties	55
8. The Weather In The Fifties	73
9. The Weather In The Sixties	79
10. The Weather In The Seventies	98
11. The Weather In The Eighties	107
12. Into The Nineties	115
Glossary of Common Weather Terms	125
Acknowledgements	126
Index	127

INTRODUCTION

by
Bill Foggitt

On 29th June 1927, father, mother, my younger brother and sister and I sat on a crowded hillside in Wensleydale around the hour of 6 am waiting to see that rare phenomenon, a total eclipse of the sun.

'This won't happen again until August 1999,' said father, 'so someone ought to take notes.' As the eldest of the family, 14 years of age, the 'lot' fell on me, and on that day I began a weather diary which I have kept up to the present time.

I remember how we gazed at the sun through pieces of smoked glass, waiting for the long-expected moment when the moon's shadow would creep slowly across the solar disc. An eerie chill darkness came upon us. The birds' shrill dawn chorus abruptly ceased, recommencing a few minutes later when the great shadow had passed on.

When I began my diary I was following a family tradition. In South Villa, the large Victorian house at Thirsk extended by grandfather William to house his 13 children, were family weather records going back 180 years. Another schoolboy, Thomas Foggitt, my great-grandfather, remembered as a pupil at Yarm grammar school being told by *his* grandparents of a great cloudburst in November 1771 which swept away a large part of Yarm with the loss of 30 lives.

It was accounts of this disaster which set great-grandfather keeping weather records day by day in the hope that he would eventually be able to predict on-coming catastrophes.

Great-grandfather commenced his weather diaries and records during the period most meteorologists term the last Little Ice Age, which lasted from the 15th century to the early 19th century. Before the Thames embankment was constructed in the 19th century, London's wide and sluggish river often froze over. In severe winters the ice was sometimes thick enough to support Frost Fairs with shops and side-shows and other activities such as ox-roasting. In 1778 the river froze over for nine weeks. The last Frost Fair took place in 1814, when an elephant walked on the Thames.

Great-grandfather (1809-1885) had the honour of being born at the end of the last Little Ice Age, but my records taken daily here at Thirsk throughout the last decade appear to indicate that we could well be sliding towards another great freeze. Some astronomers aver that these Little Ice Ages come round about every 180 years or so, which means that we could well be entering one at any time now, and my own daily temperature records from recent years seem to confirm this. Most probably it has already started!

I commenced my weather diary in 1927 but I first became interested in the subject during the late spring of 1921 when I moved at the age of eight with my family from a small terraced house to South Villa, which had a large garden sheltered by trees. But what really fascinated me was the aneroid barometer hanging in the hall and the maximum and minimum thermometer suspended (in the shade of course) on the outer wall. These were the instruments which my grandfather (who lived at South Villa from 1881 to his death in 1917) used for making a daily record of the weather for his own personal diary and for the Meteorological Office. There was also a rain gauge in the back garden.

From 1916 to the time of his death at the age of 76 in 1934, my Uncle Tom, who lived near South Villa, recorded rainfall for the Meteorological Office while my father recorded maximum and minimum temperatures. When Uncle Tom died, father took over his rainfall records and continued until shortly before his death in 1962. Then my brother took over until 1968 when I stepped in. In recognition of decades of weather watching, in 1989 I was presented with a copy of Tony Soper's *A Companion to the British Countryside* by the Director General of the Meteorological Office to 'Mr W. Foggitt and family in appreciation of the rainfall observations at Thirsk from 1914 to 1989.'

This book is all about Yorkshire weather, and what we in Yorkshire have experienced of it. There are summers of intense heat and winters of bitter cold. There is the terrible damage which nature can cause through floods, droughts, hurricanes, and lightning. But these are extremes, and we must remember that the weather still also brings mild winters and those warm summers where nature covers the ground with rich colours and scents in this wonderful county of ours. Whatever the weather, I shall never tire of observing it from my home in Thirsk.

Bill Foggitt
June 1993

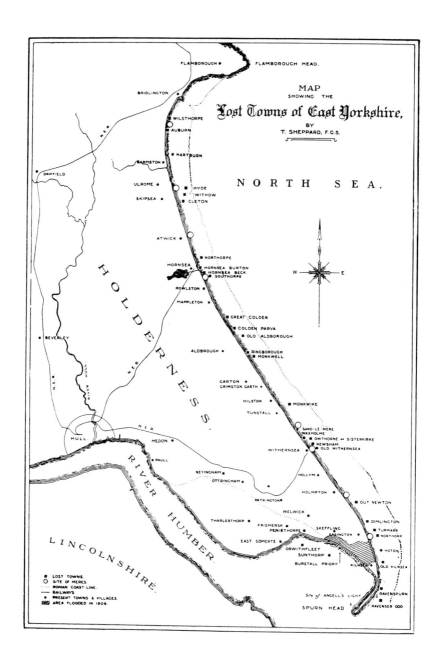

MAP
SHOWING THE
Lost Towns of East Yorkshire,
BY
T. SHEPPARD, F.G.S.

NORTH SEA.

HOLDERNESS.

RIVER HUMBER.

LINCOLNSHIRE.

SPUN HEAD.

■ LOST TOWNS.
○ SITE OF MERES.
---- ROMAN COAST LINE.
— RAILWAYS.
● PRESENT TOWNS & VILLAGES.
▨ AREA FLOODED IN 1906.

YORKSHIRE...OR WHAT'S LEFT OF IT!

Over the last millenium, millions of tons of the Yorkshire coast have crumbled into the sea. Along a seaboard stretching from the chalky redoubt of Flamborough Head to Spurn Point, thousands of acres of farmland have been pulverised by the constant attention of the tides and, despite valiant attempts at coastal protection, dozens of villages have disappeared, the entire coastline having moved several miles to the west since Roman times.

Composed of a flat, low-lying conglomeration of boulder clays interspersed with gravel and alluvial deposits, the sea cliffs have been vulnerable to erosion by powerful tidal forces. The process of attrition is further exacerbated by onshore winds and by the seepage of rainwater and the weakening action of springs, leading to some of the worst land loss in Europe.

Massive civil engineering projects costing millions of pounds have protected individual settlements, but have altered the complex interaction of tidal movements and led to aggravated erosion elsewhere. Scientists believe that the ultimate answer may lie in constructing artificial offshore reefs using millions of spent tyres and concrete. Colliery spoil has also been suggested as a suitable material and extensive trials have been conducted in recent years.

Signs of the climes – coastal erosion at Holmpton, Holderness, April 1993. (Len Markham)

A CATALOGUE OF
DESTRUCTION

1360: After suffering progressive land loss, Ravenser Odd, a thriving fishing community near Spurn Point was totally annihilated by the flooding of the Humber and the inundation of the sea.

1609: 'We find decayed by the flowing of the sea in Hornsea Beck since 1546, 38 houses, and as many closes adjoining. Also we find, since the same time, decayed in ground the breadth of twelve score yards throughout the field of Hornsey, being a mile long . . .' (unattributed).

1786: After a terrific storm, the cliff-edge church at Owthorne finally succumbed to years of encroachment. The waves undermined its foundations at the eastern end and the church toppled with a crash into the foam. '. . . Many coffins and bodies in various states of preservation were dislodged from their gloomy repositories, and strewn upon the shore in frightful disorder . . . In 1838 there was scarcely a remnant of the churchyard left.' (Poulson, writing in 1841.)

1905 – 1906: The floodbanks erected along the coast from Kilnsea to Skeffling were breached by heavy seas. Seawater contaminated farmland, crops were destroyed, wells were poisoned and access except by boat proved impossible.

Above and right: The rocky road to Spurn. This wave damaged route has now been abandoned and replaced by a new road laid on a geotextile base. (Len Markham)

Opposite: Waiting for the next tide – Claff Farm, Holmpton, Holderness ready for the long drop, April 1993. (Len Markham)

The loss of our county has been locally well publicised over the years, the subject generally receiving the gravity it deserves. However, some reports have been grossly exaggerated and not a little ludicrous as this extract from a 'popular' magazine dated 7th April 1906 shows:

'On the coast of Yorkshire there are two noses of hard rock that the sea can eat but slowly. They are Flamborough Head and Spurn Point, and between them lie 33 miles of coast, which the North Sea is swallowing at the rate of three yards in every twelve months. At Withernsea, just to the north of Spurn Point, houses go over the cliff almost daily. Some little time ago, there lived at Withernsea, an old fisherman who, despite the warnings of his friends, persisted in declaring that the sea would never harm him. . . There were two houses between the old fellow's cottage and the crumbling cliff-edge. . . One rough night, however, a biting nor'easter hurled the rampaging breakers against the shore to such purpose that first one house went and then the other. Then the wall of the old fisherman's cottage collapsed, because of the disturbance to the foundations; and he awoke in the grey of the morning to find himself looking straight ahead from his bed on the green waters of the North Sea.'

A well known fact of life in Yorkshire, erosion has not generally been of national interest. Until, that is, the morning of 4th June 1993 when a spectacular landslip in Scarborough made the national news.

Following a succession of dry summers the four-star Holbeck Hall Hotel on the resort's South Cliff began to move, but not before residents had been asked to settle their bills! The garden was lost in one catastrophic fall, and inexorably the million-pound structure moved to destruction as desperate staff raced to remove valuable antiques and heirlooms. Thousands of tourists gathered to witness the demise of the building. Hotel resident Dorothy Gledhill of Saddleworth remarked, 'I got up and looked

The death throes of the Holbeck Hall Hotel at Scarborough. What remained of the hotel after the catastrophic land slip was demolished by contractors in July 1993. (Yorkshire Post Newspapers Ltd)

out of the window – and the rose gardens had gone.' Another guest, Mrs Dorothy Fenton from Leeds applauded staff for their quick and decisive action. 'The staff came to deliver tea next door and I was annoyed because they were making a noise. They couldn't open the door because it was jammed and cracks were appearing in the ceilings.' Devastated joint shareholder of the hotel's owning group, Joan Turner, lamented, 'It is a nightmare. I was in the main lounge this morning and I could see the walls cracking in front of me. The windows were breaking and I was told to get out for my own safety.'

THE WEATHER
IN THE EARLY YEARS

1165: A Devil of a Tornado

A Yorkshire monk chronicled the appearance of the Devil,
describing the apparition as a black horse seen galloping across
a Scarborough hillside. As conclusive evidence he cited deep
hoof-prints running in a line across the dale. Modern historians
have suggested the otherwise highly imaginative text may be a
commentary on the manifestation of a tornado. Tornadoes have
been known to suck trees, roots and all from soft ground and in
the past they have invariably caused soil disturbance. In ancient
drawings and illuminated manuscripts, tornadoes are often
depicted with devils' heads.

29th March 1461: 37,000 Killed During Blizzard

One of the most momentous days of the Wars of the Roses broke
cold and grey, a mischievous wind fanning the camp fires of two
opposing armies. On Palm Sunday morning 50,000 Lancastrians
and 60,000 Yorkists mustered on Towton Moor near Tadcaster
to contest what would be the bloodiest battle ever fought on
English soil.

The hostilities commenced mid-morning as the wind freshened and snow began to fall from a darkening sky. Taking advantage of the blinding storm which flew full in the faces of the Lancastrians, the Yorkist bowmen unleashed furious showers of arrows and then retreated, their tactical manoeuvres going unseen under the curtain of snow. The Lancastrians in turn emptied their quivers, but the arrows fell short. And then the Yorkists advanced again and delivered another volley of death.

Hand to hand fighting was joined, the carnage of sword and axe staining the snow crimson. The Cock Beck ran red with blood and the melee continued unabated for ten hours, the warriors fighting 'as if the battle was the Gate of Paradise'. With the arrival of reinforcements fortunes swung in favour of the white rose and the Yorkists declared a victory, hacking off the heads of the vanquished as grisly souvenirs.

1564: Ouse Bridge Swept Away

A great flood raced through York and swept away its bridge. Twelve houses built precariously on the structure were lost with their inhabitants.

25th February 1674: Frozen to the Saddle

'A great snow began to fall about eight in the morning, and continued for four days with little intermission, the frost at the time being very severe. The whole country was covered several feet deep, and every description of business was brought to a standstill. Many persons were frozen to their saddles, and, according to the record of the time, saddle and man were removed from the horses together.' (*Annals of Yorkshire* by John Mayhall.)

18th February 1686: Steeple-high Flood

A tempest visited the villages of Kettlewell and Starbotton in Craven with such violence, that a 'hill on one side opened and cast up water into the air to the height of an ordinary church steeple'. A number of houses were demolished, every stone being swept away.

18th Century Weather Notes

7th May 1738: Sunday devotions in Holmfirth were disrupted by a severe thunderstorm. Water forced its way into the parish church and the congregation showed 'great consternation and alarm as the water rose to a considerable height in the pews'.

1740: In a remarkably intense period of sustained frost and freezing temperatures, birds fell to the ground petrified in flight, trees split asunder under the weight of accumulated ice and rock-solid bread defied eating. To commemorate the harsh conditions, printing presses were set up on the frozen Ouse and handbills were sold to skaters.

1754: A cloudburst struck the North York Moors between Thirsk and Helmsley causing extensive flooding in both towns. Thirsk's Finkle Street bridge was swept away.

On 19th April at about eleven o'clock at night an earth tremor was felt in York and surrounding villages. Simultaneous shocks rocked the astonished inhabitants of Whitby and Hull.

1758: Such was the low-lying situation and the frequent inundations of the riverside church of St Mary in Tadcaster, that a petition was raised about the state of the Wharfe. 'It frequently breaks into the church and makes such a depth of water that the petitioners cannot assemble to Divine Service therein without imminent danger to their lives.'

1771: Northern England experienced the worst flooding on record. Half of the market town of Yarm was washed away and there was great loss of life throughout the region.

1786: Batley church tower was struck with such force by lightning that four stones, each weighing in excess of 100 lbs, were flung a considerable distance.

1795: A mass of meteor debris weighing 56 lbs fell in Yorkshire.

THE NINETEENTH CENTURY

1814: Right Royal Weather

So concerned was the Prince Regent about the effects the appalling winter conditions were having on his subjects, that on 25th January he instructed Lord Sidmouth to send an edict to the Lord Lieutenant of the West Riding.

'The very serious inconvenience to individuals and the public which is experienced throughout the kingdom, from the unusual and continued severity of the present season... His Royal Highness has been pleased to command that proper measures be immediately adopted for affording, under these circumstances, every proper relief. It is more especially His Royal Highness' wish that effectual means be resorted to for restoring...the accustomed facility of communication between London and several parts of the interior, so essential to the interests of both; and for alleviating the distress which has been occasioned among a large and meritorious class of industrious persons, by the necessary suspension of their usual employments, at this season of the year, and the consequent privations to which they have been, and are still, subservient.'

The upshot of this directive? Gangs of meritorious unemployed persons were given shovels!

1817: Let There Be Wind

In the days when wind was essential to the production of our daily bread, turning the sails of the mills that ground the corn, it was regarded with reverence and awe, its mystique heightened by strange events.

One of the strangest happenings involved the famous blacksmith-preacher Sammy Hick of Micklefield, who in the unusually calm autumn of 1817 summoned a miraculous wind.

After preaching to his flock in Knottingley, Sammy invited his parishioners to a 'love feast' at Micklefield, promising two loads of corn for the celebration bread. Unfortunately, the sails of the local windmill were still and as the date for the festivities approached there was little hope of the bread materialising. A devout Christian, Sammy never doubted in divine providence and he attended the Hicklam Mill between Hook Moor and the south end of Aberford and prayed. 'Let there be wind,' he implored and lo and behold, there was a sizable puff and the great sails turned. Flour was provided for the feast, Sammy remarking, 'The wind has been sent by Him who holds us all in His hands.'

News of the miracle quickly spread and before long numerous villagers appeared with their own bags of grain. But the air abruptly fell still and silent, for they, like St Thomas, were doubters.

26th December 1824: A Persistent Thunderbolt

Lightning struck the Penistone home of Mr Joseph Jubb, clothier. 'The electric fluid entered through the roof by the side of the chimney, where it struck a 'raddle', tearing out all the iron teeth but one. The fluid then passed through an iron stove, and

The green shoots of recovery – this willow, struck by a thunderbolt in October 1992, is already showing remarkable powers of recuperation. (Len Markham)

penetrated into a room below, where it set an umbrella on fire, driving it from the nail on which it was hanging at the top of the bed, where were sleeping a young woman and two children; but fortunately, doing no injury to any of the sleepers. It then split one of the bedposts from top to bottom. It next entered another room below, struck a tin grater that was hung against the wall, and melted part of that article. It then passed through the wall into the adjoining house, where it tore off a piece of plaster, after which it disappeared.'

4th July 1838: The Huskar Pit Disaster

The sun rose on the mining community of Silkstone as a procession of unsuspecting men and attendant boys and girls entered the local mine to start their shift. Around two o'clock in the afternoon a fierce storm erupted and for two hours a lethal combination of lightning, hail and rain lashed the ground. Silkstone village was cut off by floodwaters for seven hours, but this was a mere inconvenience. At the nearby Huskar Pit a catastrophe was unfolding.

The tremendous drenching extinguished the fire in the winding engine boiler and a message was sent to the miners advising them to retreat to the lower levels of the pit until steam could be raised. Most of the trapped workforce heeded the warnings but the children who had already spent nine hours below the surface decided to exit via a drift in Nabbs Wood.

Bedraggled and not a little scared, 40 of the young labourers attempted to escape into the open air, but before the leading children neared the portal a swollen stream near the entrance burst its banks. A torrent of water poured into the drift and quickly inundated the passage, backing up against an air door. Twenty-six children aged between seven and 17 years were drowned in seconds.

There were a number of fortunate survivors. Some of the more quick-witted older children managed to take refuge in a side passage and they survived. 'I was coming up the day hole with Elizabeth Taylor,' said Uriah Jubb. 'We heard the water coming and me and Elizabeth got into a slit in the day hole, and we stopped there till we could get out. The slit is a good way past the door and near the mouth of the day hole. The water met the others as they were coming up and drove them against the door where they were drowned.'

A number of the little bodies were piled one on top of the other and extrication was a pitiful task. The corpses were removed to a makeshift mortuary and cleaned before the dreadful task of conveying them to their homes was begun. Parents wailed uncontrollably, some mothers tearing hair from their scalps in utter grief.

The children were buried on 7th July 1838. Hundreds of people crowded into the cemetery to pay their respects to the lines of coffins. The girls were buried in three graves – Catherine Garnet (8), Anne Moss (9), Elizabeth Carr (13), Hannah Webster (13), Ellen Parker (15), Elizabeth Hollin (15), Hannah Taylor (17), Sarah Jukes (8), Sarah Newton (8), Mary Sellars (10), and Elizabeth Clarkson (11). Four graves held the remains of the young boys – James Burkinshaw (7), Amos Wright (8), George Burkinshaw (10), Isaac Wright (12), Samuel Horne (10), William Allick (12), Francis Hoyland (13), James Clarkson (16), George Lamb (8), George Barnett (9), Eli Hutchinson (9), John Simpson (9), John Gothard (8), William Walmsley (8), and James Turton (10).

February 1845: Tide Spoils The Bread

The long-suffering wives of the Kilnsea lifeboatmen must have felt they should first qualify as ships' cooks, such was the affinity of the North Sea with their ovens! The most desolate and vulnerable spot in the whole of Yorkshire, Spurn Point was constantly assailed by the winds and the tides, and yet it was strategically placed for the monitoring of shipping in the Humber. And where the brave recruits of Trinity House went, their dutiful spouses were sure to follow.

What a posting! No shops, no school, no church, no pub, no trees, no neighbours – but plenty of sea. 'It filled the houses halfway up the ovens, wet the beds, wasted our fresh water with the casks floating away, broke away the fencing and washed away the coals, and left the houses in a very wretched state. We expected every wave to burst the doors in for it came with such fury that we had no time to secure anything, having to attend the crews of stranded vessels to get on shore with their boats. Our wives and the infants having to be upstairs without the fires on account of the chimneys smoking and when they came down the floors were an inch thick with mud that the water had brought in and left.'

5th February 1852: Bilberry Breached!

After a spate of heavy rains the Bilberry Reservoir at the head of the Holme Valley burst its banks, causing a trail of devastation. Just before midnight, 300,000 tons of water, a tidal wave estimated at 86 million gallons, was unleashed on the sleeping population of Holmfirth.

'It would seem as if the whole body of accumulated waters had tumbled down the valley together, sweeping all before them, throwing a four-storey mill down like a thing of nought, tossing steam-engine boilers about like feathers, and carrying death and destruction in their progress.' The waters claimed 78 lives and wholly destroyed four mills, ten dye-houses, nine stores, 27 cottages, seven tradesmen's houses, seven shops, seven bridges,

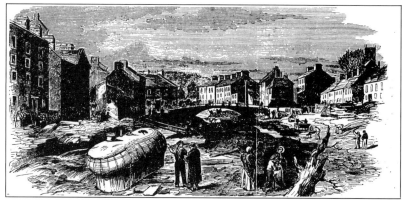

The village of Holmfirth, from Victoria Bridge — The London Illustrated News, March 6, 1852

View from Mill Hill towards Victoria Bridge — The London Illustrated News, March 6, 1852

three places of worship and two iron foundries. Over 700 people were thrown out of employment as a result of the tragedy, the estimated cost of the damage totalling nearly £250,000.

6th and 7th August 1857:
Terror Storm Swamps Scarborough

Breathing a refreshing sigh of relief after a prolonged period of fine, hot weather, Scarborians welcomed the rain that arrived on Wednesday, 5th August. But relief turned to apprehension and fear as the brewing storm, fanned by a gusting north-east gale, brought havoc to the town.

The rain lashed down in relentless torrents for over 30 hours, deluging Scarborough in an estimated 6,272 million gallons of water. Inadequate drains and sewers soon burst, all gaslights in the town were extinguished as water cascading down Burr Bank and Long Grease inundated the gasworks, and hundreds of houses, shops, factories and churches were flooded to a depth of several feet.

Bathing machines were washed out to sea, tombs and gravestones were dislodged from St Mary's churchyard and hundreds of tons of cliffside under the castle were spilled onto cottages below. Quay Street was badly affected and Mr Joseph Salmon's public house was filled with a stinking morass washed from the debris of several privies. Mrs Salmon, by no means a slight lady, was unceremoniously removed from the inn by the floodwater and deposited on a neighbour's window sill!

Aberdeen Terrace was swamped in a five foot deep lake, and in the slum William Street area dozens of poor families lost pigs, drowned in their sties, although a number of stranded horses were saved.

Scouring floodwaters rushed along Columbus Ravine causing great damage to roads and embankments, and at Peasholm, Mr Fowler's cottage was filled with water. Amongst the floating furniture a wooden cradle bore a child who slept on unconcerned.

The Queen Street/Cross Street district was pulverised by the onrush of water, so deep that a caged parrot suspended from the ceiling of the home of Mrs Fligg was drowned. The flood swept along Dumple Street and Friargate where it gushed into the Quakers' Meeting House and in St Sepulchre Street it smashed

WRECK SALE

WILL BE AUCTIONED PUBLICLY

AT THE

WHALER'S ARMS INN, WHITBY

at 10 o'clock in the forenoon on

THURSDAY, DECEMBER 13th 1828

the remaining cargo and effects of the Schooner "BOUNTY," Master, Gabriel Stranton, which foundered on Whitby Sand in a great storm on the 8th day of September, 1828, on route to London the following goods, whole or partly damaged, consisting of:-

Dried Fish, Oak Planking, Whale Oil, Iron Flax, Hemp
1400 Staves, Ashes, Sailcloth
115 pieces of exceeding fine oak timber and a few oak handspikes
3000 Oakpipe and hogshead staves
400 Pieces of fine oak timber. Rope and ships fittings.

Accommodation and refreshments will be provided at the Whaler's Arms inc   of good stabling.

32

the main sewer, contaminated effluent adding to the problems. Even elevated parts of the town suffered, residents of York Place and Harcourt Place also counting the cost.

Aided by willing holidaymakers, local people, some half-naked and suffering from exposure, struggled to salvage their belongings. Although the terrible floods claimed no lives, the phenomenon resulted in much misery and over £30,000 worth of damage was caused, according to the wise men of the corporation, by a 'long prevalence of excessive heat during the summer'.

3rd and 4th December 1858: Kilnsea Lifeboat Log

'10.30 am   Heavy NW gale. A sloop came on shore near the old cottages, no person being on board.

Noon   A perfect hurricane WNW, the weather very hazy. In the intervals of clear weather saw several vessels running out of the Humber apparently parted or slipped from their anchors.

PM   Saw a large ship dismasted and a schooner full of water. Large quantities of wreck washing on shore.

8 pm   Picked three boats up marked *Betsy* of Blyth, *Richard* of Ipswich and one no name on her. One boat picked up by countrymen had a dead man in her.

10 pm   The ship that was dismasted came on shore near the sloop, her name was *Levant* of Fredericks-haven. The sloop's name: *Neptune* of Gravelines.

4th fore part	Blowing hard NW.
Noon	More moderate.
PM	Wind SW – five vessels to be seen on Trinity Sand, two of them on their broadsides, another full of water.
Latter part	Fresh breeze.'

9th February 1861: The Gallant Lifeboatmen

Death and heroism marked one of the worst storms ever to batter the east coast, when hurricane-force winds badly affected the port of Whitby.

After rescuing the crews of a number of floundering vessels – the *Gamma*, the *Clara*, the *Roe* and the *Utility* – the coxswain of the lifeboat turned his attention to the imperilled *Merchant*. The battered ship ran aground only yards from safety but it was caught in a vortex of water and smashed to matchwood. The lifeboat too was pulverised and all but one of the crew perished.

The lone survivor, RNLI Silver Medal winner Henry Freeman said, 'When the boat turned over I was underneath her with the gun'ale across my chest. My body was under the boat and I was looking upwards through the water. A sea struck the boat and released me and I floated free. I was wearing a new kind of cork belt, which had been sent down for trial, like the ones now used. I was the only man wearing one in the boat.'

11th March 1864: Once A Sheffield Flood

Violent spring rains deluged Sheffield's newly created Dale Dike Reservoir to the west of the town. Alarmed at the ferocity of the wind and the mounting waves, the resident engineer inspected the dam embankment. Satisfied that all was well, he returned home to Sheffield for tea.

Two hours later, a workman noticed a narrow crack at the side of the embankment. After conferring with a neighbour it was decided to notify the water authorities. A horse was readied and a young lad was despatched hot-foot to Sheffield to raise the alarm. Having problems with his saddle, the lad stopped in Damflask and mentioned his errand. Fearful, the cottagers watched at the windows as the storm increased in fury.

Around midnight, oil-skin wearing engineers inspected the damage, lanterns bobbing in the wind. Deciding that pressure on the dam had to be relieved, they wrestled with the overflow pipes and, using gunpowder, they tried to blow a hole in the dam side. All to no avail. The reservoir was brimful, water was cascading over the spillway and the explosives were wet. The engineers retreated to safety as the embankment collapsed and 114 million cubic ft of water was released.

The wall of water surged down the valley engulfing Low Bradfield, Damflask and Malinbridge. Mills, cottages and bridges were swept away, the backwash surged up the Rivelin Valley and the Hillsborough and Owlerton meadows were flooded. Augmented by water from several mill dams, the torrent reached the Don, gas lamps in Neepsend Lane were quenched and the flood roared on to Brightside where it abated. Forty minutes after the catastrophic failure of the dam, one of the worst peacetime disasters ever to afflict a British city was over.

In all, 240 people died, 693 animals were drowned, 15 bridges and 100 buildings were utterly destroyed and 4,000 homes were flooded. An eye-witness to the devastation, Joseph Dyson, wrote:

'March 11th 1864 was a day never to be forgotten by those who remember. I had finished a week's lectures at Wakefield and returned by last train to Sheffield arriving at Wicker station about eleven o'clock.

On reaching Wicker Bridge I stood awhile to look over, little thinking that at that very moment a flood had started. Had I been half an hour later in the Wicker I must have perished, for the water was eight ft deep where I had just passed.

I lived in Bond Street. People all the night through kept thundering at my door. I wondered if Sheffield folk had gone daft. But I was tired and allowed the door thundering to go on. At last a "thunderer" came. He meant to get me down. On opening the door he said, "Oh, there's been an awful flood, and likely half of Sheffield drowned."

On going down past the old Town Hall I saw folk coming up ankle deep in mud. Over Wicker Bridge were trees and debris, a cow and much more. Across, near the Corner Pin, was a heap of mud about a yard high. A boy had his shirt sleeves rolled up to the shoulders and dived into the mud fishing out books. I gave him a few coppers for one, *Ovid's Poems*, supposed to come from Dam Flask school. I have it now. A woman was found under the heap.

I walked the whole course up to the dam. On reaching the embankment I noticed that the part in the centre was like a "V". The water running out was about a yard wide. Only a dozen folk were there. Eh! I could write a book about it.'

*Top: The remains of Hillsborough Bridge, Sheffield, March 1864.
Bottom: Damaged Waterloo Houses – note the altercation at number
29! (Both photographs courtesy of Sheffield City Libraries)*

March 1883: The Krakatoa Volcano

Bill Foggitt writes: 'My grandfather William Foggitt commenced taking daily weather records (temperatures and rainfall) at his home here at Thirsk on 1st January 1881. Grandfather William had been recording for two years when, after lying dormant for 200 years, the volcano Krakatoa, located in Sunda Strait between Java and Sumatra, erupted in March 1883 to produce probably the biggest explosion in history. This great blast threw millions of tons of debris many miles into the air, and falling ash was distributed over 300,000 square miles. In 15 days, volcanic dust from the explosion had encircled the earth. The violent activity of Krakatoa was responsible for the generation of huge tidal waves, some as much as 100 feet in height, which destroyed hundreds of villages and drowned an estimated 36,000 people.

'Readers may well be wondering at this point – however could the weather in Yorkshire be affected by a volcanic eruption all those many miles away? But grandfather's records appear to show that the weather *was* very much affected here at Thirsk. His records show that March 1883 was the second coldest March of our family records, with a mean temperature at Thirsk of 7.3°F below average. This was due mainly to 25 nights with air frost. But the indirect cause of the severity of the month could well be volcanic dust blotting out the sun's heat. Furthermore, my father used to tell me that grandfather often mentioned the remarkably brilliant colours of the sunset sky throughout that month. They were caused by atmospheric dust acting as a prismatic filter and were similar to those which occurred around the time when the volcano St Helens erupted in Canada in 1980.'

19th Century Spits and Spots

1814: In January, nearly all inland navigation in the West Riding was stopped by the recurring frost.

1815: Between Wakefield and Huddersfield a large waterspout was seen in the mid heavens. A large black cloud resembling an inverted cone of great length almost touched the earth. The spectacle lasted for half an hour, then rain descended in torrents.

1823: Following the severe damage inflicted by the preceding harsh winter, the spire of Wakefield cathedral was dismantled and rebuilt.

A severe gale in January wrecked the windmill in Windmill Lane, Yeadon.

Over 30 inland waterway vessels were sunk on 4th December in the wake of a tremendous storm. A cargo of flour and grain was lost on the canal near Kildwick and a number of barges foundered in Selby.

1825: On 4th January, Wakefield was bathed in extraordinary moonlight. Small print could be read in the glow, said by many to be superior to candlelight.

Such was the mild October that market gardeners harvested a second crop of strawberries in Wakefield.

1834: The modernised mill in Yeadon was again put out of action by high winds, 'part of the sails and the fan were blown away to the distance of 300 to 400 yards'.

1838: On 7th September the steam ship *Forfarshire* left Hull en route for Dundee. Butting a north-easterly breeze and persistent showers she made slow progress. After ten laborious hours she sustained a boiler leak off Flamborough Head as the wind freshened to gale force. Some time later she ran aground on Big Harcar on the Outer Farne islands. Nine passengers were rescued by the lighthousekeeper and his 23 year old daughter Grace Darling.

1839: In January, a hurricane swept through Howdenshire and caused untold damage in settlements north of the Humber. St Clement's church in Blacktoft, an important ferrying point on the Ouse, had its walls damaged and its roof blown off in the storm. Deemed beyond repair, the church was subsequently demolished.

In the Yorkshire Dales, Burnsall lost its maypole to a 'very wild night'.

A storm damaged part of the choir of Whitby Abbey.

1840: The textile industry in the hamlet of Kildale was dealt a mortal blow on 22nd July. Torrential rain on the moors surged down the valley, 'water rushing and carrying down two stone bridges and coming down the defile of the Leven with great fury and rapidity'. A 40 ft wall of water destroyed the ruins of Kildale corn mill (one of the earliest in Cleveland, this mill was devastated by a similar flood in 1324) and sped on, smashing sluice gates, an earthen dam and the local bleaching mill. The waters rushed on to damage property in Easby and Great Ayton before finally cascading over the parapet of Ayton's stone bridge.

1843: On 20th January, 37° of frost was recorded in Sheffield. A sheep-roasting party was held on the frozen river Don just above Iron Bridge. The nearby canal was frozen for seven weeks and 20 men and 22 horses were constantly employed in breaking up the ice to maintain navigation.

1860: On 16th June, heavy snow on Cross Fell caused deep drifts. The night-time temperature fell to several degrees below zero.

1870: Thomas Jackson Foggitt enjoyed a spectacular auroral display at his Thirsk home on the nights of 24th and 25th October, recording in his diary 'that people in Thirsk and district ran out into the streets thinking that they were watching the reflection of some terrific conflagration.'

1871: In one of the worst February storms in decades, the North Shields schooner *Mary* was dismasted off the notorious Flamborough Head. Without steerage, driven by the gale in the direction of Filey Brig, the craft was in danger of being engulfed until the Filey lifeboat came to the rescue. The entire crew were saved minutes before the stricken vessel hit the rocks and was smashed to matchwood.

After a succession of storms, part of the cliff-edge cemetery of St Mary's parish church, Whitby, was lost to the sea. The grisly contents of a number of coffins fell down the cliff and had to be reinterred.

1875: Killingholme high lighthouse was struck by lightning on 4th June. Part of the dome over the lantern was torn away and the light was rendered inoperative.

1881: Grandfather William Foggitt recorded the average January temperature at 12°F below normal – an all-time low for the family record books. Throughout the month, the night-time temperature was well below average for 29 nights, daytime temperatures failed to climb above freezing point on 14 separate days and in the middle of the month, there were five successive days of violent blizzards.

1887: Grandfather William again entered record-breaking statistics for the exceptionally dry month of June, recording a mere 0.17 inches of rain and five days with temperatures of 80°F and over.

1891: The long established Zetland point-to-point steeplechase was postponed as a consequence of the unseasonal March frosts and deep snow drifts.

Following a mild February, an abrupt change in the weather brought snow falls to a depth of four feet in the Castle Bolton and Preston areas of Wensleydale. A shivering 17° of frost did much damage to young fruit trees.

1893: Swanland windmill was critically damaged in a gale. Such was the force of the blast that the fantail was transported three miles!

1894: On 22nd December, a great gale tore through Sheffield demolishing an engine-house chimney at Tinsley. Five people were killed.

1895: The winter was one of the severest on record and was a talking point in the Foggitt household for years afterwards. In Sheffield, biting frost persisted for many weeks. Water mains were frozen solid in all parts of the city and water had to be supplied by carts. Nationally, the problem was so bad that the authorities introduced new bye-laws stipulating that frost-vulnerable water mains should be sunk much deeper than hitherto.

Bill Foggitt recalls 'I often heard my parents talking about that winter; and after mentioning it in a weather talk to a men's forum a few years ago an old gentleman told me how he had narrowly escaped serious injury, or worse, when the horse he was riding fell on top of him on the frozen road. In 1895 January was 8.7°F below average, February 11.3°F below and March 1.5° below.'

THE TWENTIETH CENTURY
1900–1930

12th July 1900: Ilkley's Great Flood

In the lee of a romantic moor, Ilkley had always cause to smile sweetly on the protecting heights. But then one stormy afternoon the heavens opened and the little Wharfedale town had cause to regret its kinship.

Above the moor there was a congress of inky black clouds attended by lightning and reverberating claps of thunder. Around two o'clock in the afternoon the rains came and soon, torrents of water were pouring off the precipitous moor, the swollen ghylls and becks carrying mud and debris into the town.

At a great speed of knots, water rushed through the streets, tearing up roadways, sweeping away allotments and gardens and demolishing buildings. Hundreds of chickens were drowned, in Brogden's coaching works in Chapel Lane a man died when the foundations of the building were undermined, and in Westwood Drive the floodwaters deposited huge piles of rocks and boulders, some up to half a ton in weight.

The storm raged for a little over two hours causing unprecedented damage and destruction estimated at between £50,000 and £70,000.

The Great Snowstorm – Wakefield Road, Horbury, 1906. (Wakefield Libraries)

3rd June 1908: Terrible Floods In Skipton

In a few short minutes, ruptured storm clouds brought havoc to Skipton and nearby villages. A cloudburst spewed tons of water on the surrounding fells and torrents surged down the hillsides uprooting trees, demolishing dry-stone walls and carrying huge boulders and sand. Skipton town and the Castle Woods and Embsay districts were badly affected.

The full fury of the storm was unleashed over the Thorpe and Cracoe Fell and Barden was inundated. Roads at Stirton-with-Thorlby were wasted, Bog Lane and Culvert Lane almost 'being torn from end to end,' explained the *Craven Herald*. Bonny Burnsall also suffered . . . 'part of the village green is covered with stones, gravel and other debris . . . A similar fate, but more severe, has befallen the bridge over the stream at the boundary known as Garralgum Wood. Here scores of tons of huge boulders and debris have been brought down the hillside, and after leaving portions of the road, the water cut the ground below to a depth of over 30 ft.'

Several interesting photographs depicting damage in Skipton accompanied the article, one captioned 'The dockyard on the other side of the canal also covered with water' and another 'Millholme Shed... The flood swept away the end wall, exposing the machinery and filled the shed with water and debris to the depth of many feet, covering the looms with soil and wreckage, and rendering many useless.'

Weather Notes 1900 – 1930

1900: Lumb Clough Bridge on the moors near Silsden was washed away in a cloudburst.

A typical August Bank Holiday – Westgate, Wakefield, 1922. (Wakefield Libraries)

1903: One of the coldest and wettest summers and autumns in the Foggitt records, with October producing over seven inches of rainfall above average.

1905: Exceptionally severe frosts throughout the month of January created the ideal conditions for skaters on the frozen Ripon Canal and the river Ure. Large crowds gathered on the canal banks at Bondgate Green, some intrepid icemen setting off to skate to Boroughbridge.

1906: A record temperature of 91°F was reached on 3rd September in Sheffield.

1911: Bill Foggitt: '9th August brought the highest recorded temperature for Britain; 100°F at Kew, London. My father, a chemist's assistant in London at the time, was walking in St James' Park during the afternoon of that day and often related how, like Arthur Askey many years later, he watched the flowers fading "before his very eyes"! Here at Thirsk that day my grandfather recorded 96°F. On 19th August 1932 my father recorded 98°F, and a pretty close runner up was 91°F which I recorded on 3rd August 1990! In 1911, the mean temperature for that month was 3°F above average; every month of 1911 was warmer than average apart from March and October.'

1914: Just a few months into the First World War, on 16th December 1914, Scarborough sat down to breakfast unaware that mortal danger lurked in the early morning fog. From the Wilhelmshaven base, a powerful German battle group under the overall command of Admiral Franz von Hipper had steamed undetected to shell the peaceful Yorkshire town. The bombardment commenced at 8.05 am. In a 20 minute barrage over 500 high explosive shells were hurled against the resort causing excessive damage, injuring 80 residents and killing 17 more.

1917: It became known as The Soldiers' Winter, as temperatures fell to 4°F and 5°F below the average for January and February. The coldest night in the Foggitt records for the present century came on 1st April, with 32°F of frost. Wakefield experienced a low of −14°C.

1919: Very heavy snowfalls hit Yorkshire and northern England during the first Armistice Day services, 11th November. Sheffield and the Peak District had the heaviest snowfall in 40 years.

1920: A Howden airship piloted by an American crew crash landed near Guisborough in worsening weather. In February, a soup kitchen was opened in the Market Stall House, Blossomgate, Ripon to relieve the hardship caused by continuing cold weather. On 18th June, hailstones the size of marbles pelted the Vale of York. The night time temperature dropped to freezing point.

1927: Around 6 am, the dawn chorus abruptly ceased as hundreds of people gathered in Leyburn to witness a spectacular event not to be repeated again until 1999. The solar eclipse was subsequently blamed for the damp summer which saw the extensive flooding of fields and hedgerows and a poor harvest.

1929: The severest February since 1895. Bill Foggitt recalls: 'I was a boarder at a school at Scarborough that winter and the ground was frozen so hard it prevented us playing football throughout the month of February – a relief for me as most weekday afternoons we had walks along the beach instead, which I greatly enjoyed. I was saddened, though, to see the frozen corpses of numerous seabirds, mosty cormorants.

On Monday 11th February, my mother found her washing hanging on the line frozen stiff, the only time in her life that this happened.'

THE WEATHER
IN THE THIRTIES

23rd July 1930: Lifeboat Rescue Two Miles Inland

In what was the wettest summer in the Foggitt records for the present century, the Whitby lifeboat was pressed into service at Ruswarp, two miles *inland*. Bridges were washed away in Sleights and Egton Bridge and there was much destruction to residential, commercial and farming property over a wide area.

A slow moving low centred off Lincolnshire brought heavy rain on four successive days. The peak downpour came on the 22nd. Over the period, 5.2 inches of water fell in Danby and Castleton had 11.97 inches. Converging floods threatened the complete inundation of Whitby and there was mounting fear of drowning. The *Whitby Gazette* of Friday, 25th July tells the desperate tale:

'DEVASTATING STORMS AND FLOODS . . . PLEASURE BOATS CARRIED OUT TO SEA . . . THRILLING RESCUE AT RUSWARP AND THE CARRS.

'The worst floods of which there is any record occurred on Wednesday morning in the area drained by the river Esk and its tributaries. Following a period of fairly settled weather a small shower was brought up by an easterly wind on Sunday afternoon, and with a rapidly falling barometer the wind

No highway...and no railway; the devastating floods in Whitby, July 1930.

strengthened to a gale at dusk, followed by a heavy downpour of rain which persisted all night. By Monday morning the barometer had steadied, but the backing of the wind to the north and north-west in the afternoon foretold an unsettled period, though the mercury commenced to rise.

'Rain continued to fall on Tuesday morning and there was a heavy fresh down the river, the Ruswarp and the Carrs being covered by from two to three ft of water, disorganising the bus service to Sleights, the journey having to be made by way of Carr Hill Lane. The rain was general over the whole district and the ford at Barnby Becks was reported impassable, there being between six and eight ft of water. By the riverside the continuance of rain caused the greatest anxiety, and the rising of the river became so alarming that some people in the low-lying places on Ruswarp and Carrs left their homes and took refuge with friends and neighbours.

'Shortly after midnight rain commenced to pour from a sky of inky blackness and became a veritable downpour. The fresh water coming down the river assumed alarming proportions and fears of disaster were not without foundation. The first untoward event in the harbour was the breaking from her moorings of the steam tug *Beechwin*. There were even more serious happenings at Briggswath. Many people were alarmed but had no idea of the calamity which was to fall upon them. At four-thirty on Wednesday morning the river had risen to a raging torrent and it was seen that unless there was an early abatement something of an untoward nature was bound to occur. People in the vicinity were aroused when the water began to rise up the roadway leading over from Woodlands. By five o'clock the river was running over the roadway at Briggswath, and in an hour the water had increased to a depth of two ft. Consternation seized the people in the houses, and at six o'clock, when it seemed that Briggswath would be washed away, the weight of the water proved too much for the massive stone bridge. A crack appeared

50

in the roadway at the Briggswath side and in less time than it takes to record, the whole of the bridge and its two stone piers were swept away.'

The awesome power of the flood was more than matched by the indomitable spirit of the Whitby lifeboatmen. Up the raging Esk they came to Ruswarp to rescue marooned families, the boat being hauled through the narrow streets by many willing hands.

1931: 'September Either Dries Up Ditches Or Breaks Down Bridges.'

The truth of this old Yorkshire adage was put to the test in September when for the second time in 15 months torrential rain swamped Whitby. The floods also inundated many Eskdale villages, as the report in the *Whitby Gazette* of 11th September 1931 shows.

1931. A flooded Stamford Bridge Corn Mill alongside the A166/river Derwent. The picnic was enjoyed regardless – see roof rack! (Mrs V Priest)

Top: Penistone High Street, March 1933. (Mr C Hitchin)
Bottom: A young Bill Foggitt stands alongside 40 feet high snowdrifts at Sutton Bank, March 1933. (Bill Foggitt)

'July 1930 and September 1931 will be chronicled for devastating floods affecting Whitby, Ruswarp, Sleights, Grosmont, Egton, Glaisdale, Lealholm, Danby and Castleton. Last year's flood resulted in loss of life, the suspension of Whitby's water supply and the carrying away of Sleights' road bridge . . . whereas the floods of July 1930 came in the night, this time the flood danger became imminent during the day, giving ample warning enabling many residents to remove their belongings to places of safety, yet the necessity arose for the services of the Whitby lifeboat.'

Over the Thirsk district, terrific thunderstorms on the 12th, 13th and 14th September brought the Cod Beck into spate, causing flooding in Thirsk town. 'I never dreamt that Thirsk was so like Venice,' said a young probationary Methodist minister on his first visit.

18th July 1939: The Wettest Day Of The Century

'A figure of 2.9 inches of rain was recorded by my father here at Thirsk,' recalls Bill Foggitt. 'In little over an hour, the large lawn in front of our house was completely covered by water. Total rainfall for July here was 7.25 inches, 4.47 inches above average.'

Snippets from the Thirties

1932: May was the wettest for 160 years over England and Wales. In Yorkshire, there was severe flooding of the Don Valley at Bentley.

1933: During February, Harrogate had nearly three ft of snow in three days. The winter generally was fairly mild but on Friday, 25th March, a violent blizzard swept across the North York Moors. The storm continued throughout the weekend. 'On

The river Wharfe thunders against Ben Rhydding Bridge – March 1935. (Wharfedale Newspapers)

Sunday morning, father, mother and I motored to Scarborough,' noted Bill, 'and reaching the summit of Sutton Bank where there were drifts 40 ft high, we were told by a policeman that we were the first motorists up the bank since Friday morning.'

1938: The aurora borealis was visible in the county on the 25th and 26th January, and, accompanied by a magnetic storm, caused scintillating and rapidly changing colour effects.

On 12th August, a myriad of hailstones fell on Wold Newton near Bridlington. So cold was the night-time temperature, that the stones remained frozen until morning.

THE WEATHER
IN THE FORTIES

1940-1945: Not Just Flak and Tracer

Bad weather accounted for hundreds of RAF crashes during the war years, capricious winds, rain, fog, snow and the problems of high altitude icing adding a meteorological gambit to the daily gamble with death.

Aircrews throughout the county were grounded for days as a result of inclement conditions. Airfields were transformed into quagmires and frustration and boredom became the new enemies, as impatient pilots, navigators and gunners scanned the skies. Ironically, fair weather was a demon in disguise, blue skies and the full moon bringing danger from enemy attack.

High risk was the daily fare of all our aviators during the Second World War even when the guns were mute.

7th December 1940: An airborne Hampden (L4103) from RAF Finningley was struck by lightning. There was an immediate engine failure and the aircraft crash-dived and hit the ground one and a half miles west of Blaxton. Both crew members were killed.

12th February 1942: In bad weather an Airacobra fighter of No 601 Squadron crash-landed on ice alongside the flooded banks of the river Ouse at Acaster Malbis, York. The pilot was drowned.

7/8th March 1943: A Bomber Command raid on Essen from the North Yorkshire base of Dishworth was abandoned because of poor conditions.

13th December 1943: 60 MU, whose role was to recover crashed aircraft, left their Shipton-by-Beningbrough base for Whernside. A Halifax bomber (DT 578 Category 'E' 2) had come to grief near the mountain's summit and wreckage was scattered over a wide area. Hampered by arctic conditions and poor visibility, the salvage team had to climb for an hour and a half each day to reach the crash site. Full recovery took several weeks.

16/17th December 1943: Two Lancaster bomber squadrons from RAF Linton-on-Ouse combined in an attack by 492 aircraft on Berlin. Some of the returning Yorkshire-based aircraft became

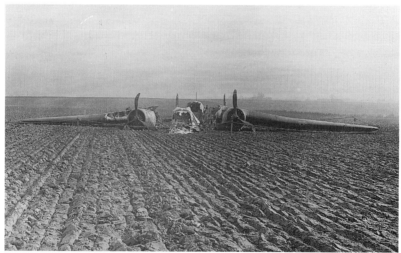

An Armstrong Whitworth Whitley bomber of 102 and 77 Squadrons after crashing on approach to Driffield, 20 February 1939.

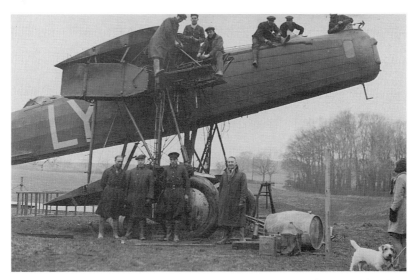

A Handley Page Heyford of 99 and 149 Squadrons after crashlanding in high winds near Bridlington, 19 April 1939. (Both photographs by kind permission of Yorkshire Air Museum, Elvington)

lost in dense fog. Circling with diminishing supplies of fuel, several Lancasters crashed. DS 779 came down between Hopperton and Hunsingore near Northlands Farm with the loss of five crew. DS 837 crashed at Yearsley and A 408 came to grief on Murton Common.

18th January 1944: Six members of the eight-man crew of a Halifax BII bomber were killed when it crashed in fog into a hillside at Black Hambleton near Osmotherley.

5th March 1945: LW219 'Y'-Yoke – a Halifax Mk VII bomber from RAF Linton-on-Ouse dropped from the sky in freezing fog. Part of a sortie of 14 aircraft bound for Germany, the Halifax laboured under the weight of full bomb and fuel loads, severe icing causing it to plummet to the ground only 21 minutes after take-off. Nunthorpe Grove in York was hit by the fuselage and an engine entered the Nunthorpe secondary school kitchen. The

A snow cutting at Townhead near Dunford Bridge, early in 1947.
(Mr C Hitchin)

pilot and all crew members except one were killed. Wireless operator/air gunner, Pilot Officer J. Low baled out just before impact. At so low an altitude death was almost certain, but miraculously the updraught of the exploding aircraft allowed his parachute to deploy. The airman hit a shed roof and was badly injured. There were five civilian fatalities and a further 18 people were injured.

The appalling conditions also accounted for the crash of Halifax NP793 of 426 Squadron. Clinging ice robbed the aircraft of steering and it came down 45 minutes after leaving Linton-on-Ouse one mile south of Hutton-le-Hole near Kirkbymoorside. All seven crew were killed on impact.

1947: Arctic Yorkshire

Debilitated by six years of strife with acute shortages of raw materials and fuel, war-weary Britain was in no position to cope with one of the worst winters of the century. For a time the whole country almost ground to a halt, the problems in the ailing mining and power industries being exacerbated by unofficial strikes and absenteeism.

Domestic conditions were grim and cheerless. Coal, gas and even candles were in short supply and many a home fire was kept burning with broken furniture and timber gathered from the hedgerows. There were frequent power cuts and only limited supplies of bread and other basic foodstuffs. Responding to Prime Minister Clement Attlee's radio appeal to economise, people ate less. They went to bed early and shared baths and, as they had dug for victory during the war years, in 1947 they dug for survival, shovels and spades on the front step ever ready to do battle with the daily onslaughts of snow.

Neither the prognostications of the weathermen nor the conditions during the early part of the winter gave an inkling of the problems ahead. However, during the sunny and quite mild Boxing Day of 1946, Bill Foggitt noted nature's warning: 'My father and I were thrilled to notice a flock of about a dozen waxwings, beautifully coloured and crested birds from northern Europe and the Scandinavian countries, devouring our cotoneaster berries in our garden. Although I have seen an odd waxwing or two in the Thirsk district, this was the only time I have seen them in my garden and so many, and I remember my father saying at the time that if the wind should get into the east, we should have a hard winter, because the arrival of these beautiful birds indicated that winter had set in early on the continent and that with persisting east winds, it would shortly arrive here.'

On 6th January, Leeds had its first snowfall of the winter. Widespread electricity cuts followed on the 7th, disrupting industry across the whole country. That night, Ilkley became the coldest place in England, recording 7°F of frost. By 8th January, loudspeaker vans were touring Sheffield centre pleading with the public not to shovel snow into roadways, after the city had experienced traffic chaos and difficulties with blocked drains. In the third week of January the blizzards arrived in earnest.

By the end of January, successive white-outs and plunging night-time temperatures had wreaked havoc. Hundreds of isolated farmsteads across the region and dozens of villages such as Thixendale on the Wolds had been cut off and in the major Yorkshire towns and cities there was a mass mobilisation of prisoner-of-war and casual labour in a desperate attempt to keep the roads open.

If January was bad, February was worse, the period from the 2nd to the 22nd being completely sunless. During these dark days there was great individual hardship but also stirring accounts of improvisation, heroism and sheer Yorkshire pluck. With coal stocks dwindling, housewives opened their doors to heat their houses. A Leeds minister walked 20 miles in the snow to take divine service, and in Barnoldswick one determined lady intent on shopping hitched a ride on a snowplough!

The weather was unrelenting. Day by day, the national crisis worsened. Bread, beer and basic foodstuffs became scarce, the cost of vegetables rose dramatically, the price of candles soared from 8½d to 10¾d per pound, shoppers were rationed to 3d worth of potatoes in the Mexborough district and, because of the dearth of potatoes and the freeze-up at sea, fish and chip shops were threatened with closure. But the worst problem of all was the grinding cold. Hundreds of old people, the weak and the infirm died of hypothermia.

In cabinet, the government debated the energy crisis. And then the elements turned the screw. The accumulating snow isolated Hubberholme and Buckden; Langstrothdale was completely cut off; thousands of sheep were buried in drifts; the snow reached roof height in Embsay; and in Normanton, then an important railway junction and marshalling yard, hundreds of laden coal waggons were frozen to the rails. Across the West Riding, up to 300,000 tons of vital fuel in 30,000 waggons was similarly ice bound. Sir Noel Holmes, chairman of the North East Region of the National Coal Board warned that 'unless these railway waggons are removed, a position will quickly be reached when there will be no empty waggons to receive the coal output.'

Coal deliveries by road and barge had to run the gauntlet of hard packed snow and ice. A five inch thick ice-sheet on the A1 was tackled with a 15 ton agricultural tiller and in Skipton the heaviest steel craft were set to work breaking up the ice and ferrying much-needed coal to the local mills. The men of the Yorkshire coalfield struggled to increase production. Sunday working was introduced but tonnages faltered and in the

Sheffield and South Yorkshire areas only 40% of opencast sites were working in early February.

Fuel shortages were so acute that thousands of workers were laid off, staple heavy engineering and textile manufacturing businesses feeling the brunt of closures. The tally of East and West Riding employees temporarily out of work was an alarming 41,093 and in rural areas there were similar problems. There was a glut of milk. Blocked roads and a shortage of bottles – thousands were buried under drifts – severely disrupted deliveries and there was rationing, particularly in schools.

Commercial establishments and the activities of local councils were also hit. The Lewis's store in Leeds had to be illuminated by hurricane lamps. In Castleford, gas street lighting was extinguished from all but main junctions, and the lamps were lit only during 'summer' hours. In nearby Wakefield all but 30 of the 800 gas lamps were lit.

Arctic conditions in the countryside killed thousands of sheep. One Airedale farmer endured the agonising sight of a ewe emerging from a snowdrift with a dead lamb frozen to its side. Over 1,000 breeding animals were buried for 14 days on the Stean and Lofthouse moors in Nidderdale and there was little hope of finding them alive. Most minor roads were impassable, one farmer lamenting, 'It is impossible to get hay to the farms even by railway. The cutting between Ribblehead and Dent is completely filled by a block of ice 20 ft deep.' Across the county at Huggate on the Wolds, snow covered the byways to a depth of twelve ft and only the tops of telegraph poles were visible. The plight of the farmers received national attention on 8th February when Miss Monica Spensley of The Farm, Thorlby near Skipton, gave graphic descriptions of her experiences rescuing sheep in a BBC broadcast.

1947 – High Peak, west of Sheffield, with quite a lot of digging still to be done. (Sheffield City Libraries)

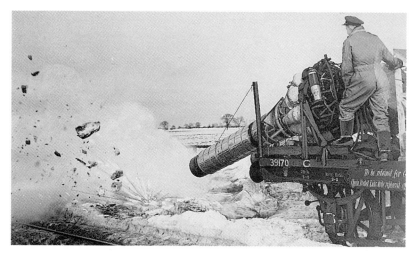

1947 – A jet engine loaned by the RAF being employed by LNER to clear snowdrifts from the Hull – Hornsea line near Swine. (Hull Daily Mail)

The arctic comparisons were complete on the 23rd when a *Yorkshire Evening News* reporter made the front page with his thrilling account of a journey 'Through Humber ice packs to Leeds'.

'"Goin' to be a funny trip this," said the skipper of the tug *Lion*, Wilfred Brooks of Southcotes Lane, Hull. "It's a great many years since I saw ice packing up the river like it is tonight."' The report goes on, 'Then we got into the pack ice. We were on a flowing tide and had a stiff easterly wind astern, but there was so much ice around that we just crawled. Large ice floes, a couple of feet thick, would thud against the tug, and sometimes the following lighters were driven off their course and out of the channel. . . . a most remarkable thing happened then. I looked outboard, and there were two members of the lighter *Mallory II* standing on the Humber. . . As the men worked, the ice below them would gradually crack, sometimes they had to jump smartly from one floe to the other . . . "I've heard about Scott and his men doing this sort of thing in the Antarctic," joked one of the lightermen, "but I never thought I'd be doing it off Blacktoft."'

On 25th February, optimistic sighs of relief could be heard across Yorkshire. 'Chance of milder weather,' declared the experts.

And then, overnight, 'Greatest Yorkshire blizzard traps scores of trains, slows coal movement . . . Nearly all East, North Riding impassable . . . Worst rail hold up in memory.'

The blizzards and sub-zero temperatures continued into March. On the 2nd, Huddersfield had 32°F of frost, and on the same day, in Wetherby, skating took place on the Wharfe for the first time since 1897. Fresh snowstorms swept the county on the 7th. A spokesman for the beleaguered Dearne Valley Traction company apologised for the spasmodic bus service. 'Eighty vehicles are out of action every day with broken springs, burst

1947 – Aftermath of the thaw in the Ilkley area. The river Wharfe burst its banks and severely disrupted traffic. (Wharfedale Newspapers)

radiators and broken chassis.' On 8th March, the blackest Saturday in peace-time football, there were 26 league postponements, followed on the 13th by yet more blizzards which caused further chaos, completely blocking 28 LNER lines in Northern England.

Relief yet trepidation. Inevitably, winter eased its grip, but with the rise in temperatures came the nightmare of flood. On 13th March, families had to abandon their homes as the Don overflowed at three points. Sharlston colliery was put out of action; 300 local roads were swamped; in York over 2,000 homes on the Tang Hall estate were inundated; and there was an exciting rescue of two kennelmaids and a trainer from the top of the Wombwell Greyhound Stadium.

By March, it was all over and the recriminations and explanations began. The bluebells shook themselves off and the arguments about our unpreparedness raged . . . but let the final word go to Mr P. Noel-Baker, Secretary of State for Air who was asked to supply an explanation in the House of Commons on 19th March about 'the incorrect weather forecasts given by his department during the recent cold spell.' 'To my regret', he replied, 'I must admit that the science of meteorology still leaves much to be desired (laughter and cheers).'

March and April 1947: A Thousand Hands To The Pumps

In two disastrous months, the most serious floods ever experienced in the history of the River Ouse Catchment Board completely devastated Selby and Barlby. Following the thawing of deep snow and the onset of heavy rainfall in the uplands through the latter half of March, flows in the Swale, Rye, Wharfe, Derwent, Aire and Ouse were at record levels, the flood gauge in York on the 24th showing a height last reached in 1831.

Bread being delivered to a resident near Selby Toll Bridge in March 1947. Hundreds of families took refuge in bedrooms as flood water swept into their homes. (Yorkshire Weekly Newspaper Group Ltd)

Augmented by exceptionally high tides, the flood waters surged against ill-maintained river defences already weakened by severe frosts, years of neglect being cruelly exposed in a number of catastrophic breaches. Millions of gallons of water poured into Selby and Barlby and outlying settlements.

At Barlby there was serious disruption of production at the Olympia Oil and Cake mills and at the British Sugar Corporation and Fletchers Sauce works. In the district, 550 houses were flooded, most of these being inundated to a depth of between three and six ft. Over 400 soldiers were deployed by the authorities to help 600 mill workers stem the tide, the *Goole Times* recording: 'The road from the toll bridge to Barlby breach was crowded with sightseers on Sunday. As far as the eye could see was water resembling a sea. The torrent sweeping through the breach held people in awe as it first rushed towards Selby and then turned eastwards towards Cliffe and Hemingbrough, finally escaping through another breach at Newhay.'

The situation in Selby was equally as bad. Financial losses in the town ran into millions of pounds, 10,000 tons of potatoes alone being ruined by the floods. Residents of Millgate, Bondgate, Ousegate, East Common and Shipyard Road fared particularly badly. Household belongings and dead horses and cattle floated through the streets, water supplies were contaminated and vital foodstuffs had to be delivered by the army, using amphibious 'ducks'. The fortitude of the town was again echoed in a *Goole Times* leader. 'The town and district of Selby, stricken and devastated this week by a flood horror unparalleled in local history is tonight holding on, fighting back and winning through its grim battle with a great inland sea.'

Using tops of telegraph poles as street guides, 'ducks' were again pressed into service around Barlby and 300 residents were evacuated to Riccall aerodrome. Castleford, Wistow, Gowdall, Snaith and York also suffered; 400 families in the Athrons

Estate, Bentley had to be rescued by amphibious vehicles; and local railway lines were closed to traffic.

The beleaguered communities were assisted by the armed forces. Northern Command provided mobile kitchens and the RAF played its part, a Lancaster bomber from the base at Lindholme near Thorne parachuting consignments of food to the residents of Wistow.

Throughout their ordeal, the flood victims showed great stoicism and determination. Already rationed, basic commodities were in short supply but neighbours displayed the Dunkirk spirit, sharing what little food they had and tirelessly helping each other to evict their unwelcome guest. With 'business as usual' resolve, some shops kept open, displaying their wares in floating trays. A funeral cortege was solemnly conducted to the church in Wistow by boat and one determined resident of Gowdall, Mr T. Walton, ferried supplies to his hens in a most ingenious fashion. Using an old zinc bath and several beer barrels, he assembled an improvised boat, paddling to his chickens with a spade!

When the floods receded the full horror was revealed. The damage and destruction were enormous and the drainage experts and water engineers had learnt a terrible lesson. What became known as the 'Great Flood of 1947' was marked by the heroic efforts of nearly all concerned. Only a very small minority of those affected betrayed their neighbours. These looters were severely dealt with.

Snippets from the Roaring forties

1940: In the Foggitt journals, January, with up to 28°F of frost, was the severest on record. Parts of the Humber froze and ice floes drifted downstream, accumulating under the Victoria Pier.

Top: Leeds Road, Selby, March 1947.
Bottom: Evacuees leaving Park Street, Selby, March 1947. (Yorkshire Weekly Newspaper Group Ltd)

Top: *Rescue by amphibious vehicle, Barlby Road, Selby, March 1947. (Yorkshire Weekly Newspaper Group Ltd)*
Bottom: *Doncaster Road, Selby, March 1947. (Associated Newspapers Ltd)*

On 26th January, a blinding snowstorm swept across the county, badly disrupting Sheffield. There was up to four ft of snow in city gardens and pavements became impassable for weeks as a consequence of compacted snow and ice.

Fifteen inches of snow fell on Pontefract on 28th January. Local bird populations were decimated.

1942: In January and February, northerly airstreams brought thick snow to eastern England.

1943: During February and March, Hull and Scarborough had no rain for 41 days.

On 7th April a 90 mph storm lashed Spurn Head.

In May, five ft deep snow drifts persisted around Moor House on Cross Fell.

1944: On Whit Monday, a cloudburst inflicted severe damage on Holmfirth. A long stretch of Woodhead Road caved in and shops in Towngate, Victoria Street, Hollowgate and Lower Mills collapsed.

1949: A brilliant auroral display was seen in Yorkshire on the consecutive nights of 25th and 26th January.

THE WEATHER
IN THE FIFTIES

31st January 1953: The Great East Coast Storm

East Yorkshire escaped the worst ravages of a storm which caused havoc along the entire East Coast, and killed some 300 people, but flooding and minor damage were widespread. From Bridlington to Spurn Point homes were inundated and village halls were hastily commandeered for evacuees. Throughout the region communications were disrupted as 90 mph winds brought down telephone lines. In Bridlington, heavy seas smashed through the doors of the Spa Royal Hall and a number of craft in the harbour were wrecked. In Hornsea and Withernsea, cinema audiences emerged to find the streets awash and Hull was also hit, the low-lying Old Town area being the worst affected.

1958: Typically British

During the winter months, Yorkshire endured the longest freeze since 1947. January was an exceptionally cold month. 26° of frost were recorded at RAF Finningley on 24th January, the snowy conditions causing the usual chaos on road and rail. In February, a battalion of 1,450 men equipped with 174 snow-shifting vehicles and 40 snowploughs contested the streets of Leeds at a cost of between £3,000 and £4,000 per day. On Ilkley

Lost in the fog. This vessel, the freighter 'Lynn Trader' ran aground at Flamborough in 1950. (Innis Studios, Hessle)

Tarn there was floodlit skating. But compared to previous bad winters it was short-lived. Temperatures rose to the lower 40s on 9th February and there was a quick thaw.

More memorable than the winter, were the typically British months of June and July. 'I was feeling indisposed one afternoon and I went to bed and missed summer,' remembered Len Markham senior from Leeds.

Following persistent daily downpours, hay rotted in fields, vegetable and fruit crops were spoiled and weed growth was prolific. County cricket fixtures were badly disrupted and there were complaints about the length of outfield grass. After the wettest spell for ten years there was an unprecedented demand for wellington boots and waterproof clothing. 'It's the biggest rush for umbrellas and plastic mackintoshes I have ever experienced in July,' said a spokesman at one Leeds store.

1959: 'Nice Weather For Prunes'

This second driest year of the century was marked by high temperatures and keen thirsts. Following a bone-dry spring, the sun beat down remorselessly during the summer months and by the end of August water stocks across the county were at their lowest levels for decades. Beer and soft drink sales soared.

Rationing schemes were prepared by waterworks managers and there were dire warnings that factories would have to close unless supplies of water were conserved. The Cringles reservoir near Silsden had dwindled to a pool a mere 40 ft in diameter, threatening production at the Silsden Dyeworks, and water had to be piped overland from the river Aire through a half-mile

'Here's a dry one, lad'. The scene in Hessle Road, Hull, 1954. (Innis Studios, Hessle)

Upperthong, near Holmfirth around Christmas, 1951. The children in the picture recall standing on top of their ice cave and removing the bulb from the street lamp; in the eskimo fashion, they ate their meals in the den and used candles. (Mrs N Coldwell)

network of pipes. In Scammonden near Slaithwaite local springs completely dried up and water had to be supplied by the West Riding Fire Service.

The banning of hosepipes was universal and standpipes were installed in many locations. The countryside was tinder dry and a number of serious moorland fires erupted, the blazes on the moors near Scammonden and Osmotherley being particularly bad. The long, dry, extended summer faded into a dull November.

Snippets from the Fifties

1951: Snow covered Cross Fell in the Pennines until 10th July.

1953: While Queen Elizabeth II was being crowned in Westminster Abbey on 3rd June, snow fell in Yorkshire. Unseasonal fires were lit as the temperature hovered around 50°F. Snow lay on the higher parts of the Pennines.

1955: In the Arctic fishing grounds atrocious weather was claiming Yorkshire lives. On 24th January, in what was Hull's biggest post-war disaster, two ice-shackled trawlers sank off North Cape with the loss of 40 lives.

Fog. This picture was taken on 27th November 1958 in City Square, Leeds. The fog was so bad it was decided to illuminate the bobby with a gas flare. (Yorkshire Post Newspapers Ltd)

In May, high level roads across the Pennines were blocked by drifts. Snow still covered the ground at Malham Tarn on the 17th.

1956: Following a prolonged hot spell in September, drought brought threats of prosecution to hosepipe users in Ripon as the army prepared to pump water from the river Ure.

1957: Earth tremors were felt in Leeds on February 11th and 13th. No damage was reported.

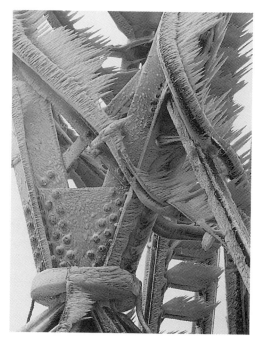

The base of Holme Moss television mast, with icicles at right angles in the sub zero temperatures and ferocious wind. Picture taken in the mid 1950s by Ken Archer.

THE WEATHER
IN THE SIXTIES

16th February 1962: 'Worst Ever' Winds Smash West Riding

At least eight people were killed and hundreds more were injured by hurricane force winds. Leeds, Bradford and Sheffield bore the brunt of the storms, damage running into many millions of pounds throughout Yorkshire.

The authorities acted speedily to warn people of the dangers of leaving home after dozens of pedestrians were blown over in Bradford, and in Leeds, the City Station was closed because of the danger of flying glass. Cowering in their beds that terrible night, householders prepared for the worst as the winds strengthened and slates and roofs were torn off and power and telephone lines brought down. One of the first fatalities was a young mother, Mrs A. Thrush of Hunslet, Leeds, who was crushed by falling timbers. The wind completely demolished scores of pre-fabricated homes in Sheffield and 176 families were made homeless. Two thousand properties were affected in Bradford and an estimated 60,000 homes were damaged in Leeds. In the surrounding countryside it was a similar tragic story.

In excess of 66,000 trees were lost around the Leeds reservoirs and 160 acres of woodland were so badly mauled that replanting was the only option. The estates at Harewood, Bramham and Rudding were also badly hit and in Harrogate the winds left a trail of destruction. Near Harlow Moor Road a 200 yard avenue of pines was flattened and damage was widespread in Harlow Carr Gardens where 100 trees and shrubs were uprooted. The disconsolate gardens director, Mr A. Sigston Thompson, said, 'I am afraid it will be 30 or 40 years before Harlow Carr looks as well planted again.'

In Otley, stalls were absent from the market place for the first time in over 30 years, although one brave soul set out his wares in the shelter of the Buttercross, losing hundreds of eggs to the wind.

On the coast, Scarborough's fishing fleet was stormbound and 90 miles per hour winds in Whitby tore off chimney pots and overturned many caravans.

Gangs of council workmen and private contractors were mobilised in Leeds and Sheffield and contingents of Royal Engineers did sterling work in both cities. On 4th March, Hugh Gaitskell visited the stricken areas of Leeds and the Queen sent a personal message of condolence and hope. 'Please convey my heartfelt sympathy to all the people in the West Riding who have suffered as a result of the recent gales. I am greatly reassured by the reports of the magnificent and untiring help which the voluntary organisations have given to the civic authorities in their joint efforts to alleviate the immediate and widespread distress.'

The unalloyed gloom was lifted by the experience of a Rotherham policeman whose helmet had been blown onto the top of the parish church in an earlier storm. The winds returned it to his head with a thump!

4th December 1962: Fog Blanket Over England

Described as the 'Devil's Brew' by one AA patrolman, a cloud of fog, laced with smoke and noxious fumes, choked 40,000 square miles of England, badly disrupting transport and causing health problems on a massive scale. Visibility in Yorkshire fell to five yards on the A1 at Ferrybridge and Knottingley and on the Wakefield to Doncaster road. Fog closed down the port of Goole; there were no sailings or arrivals on either of the two tides and seven ships lay fog-bound.

On 5th December, frightening headlines across the country reported 32 smog-attributed deaths, mostly in London, 'a city groping about in nil visibility'. Conditions were nearly as bad in the industrial West Riding. Mothers kept their children indoors and made improvised smog masks from handkerchiefs and pillow cases. The young, the old and the chronically sick were particularly vulnerable to respiratory poisoning. In Leeds, many people were admitted to hospital with chest complaints. Mr Richard Dalley, Leeds City Analyst, said, 'The sulphur dioxide figures recorded in the city were the highest ever...' Goole's senior health inspector Mr R.O. Black noted, 'Soot deposit has increased considerably this week; the amount of sulphur in the atmosphere caused by domestic fires has risen enormously.' In Huddersfield, a policeman reported for duty wearing a smog mask. It was a terrifying time for motorists. There were numerous accidents and minor shunts.

1963: Deep Freeze

As a prelude to an exceptional year, the new year dawned with nearly every part of the county covered in snow. Nationally, the atrocious weather conditions were to leave at least 49 people dead. Internationally, the below zero temperatures were to lead to the freezing of the river Danube for the first time in memory, to the Neptune fountain in Florence freezing rock solid, and to hunger-crazed wolves in central Greece attacking villagers. Here in the north of England, 77 days of unremitting cold and blizzards were to bring RAF rescues, avalanches and the blasting away of snow cornices with gelignite!

One of the severest Januaries in the Foggitt records for the present century was marked by a series of blizzards. Snow fell heavily on the east coast on 13th January reducing visibility at Flamborough Head to nil. Firemen were summoned to deliver drinking water to remote parts of Nidderdale after water supplies froze up. Thixendale, Riplingham and dozens of other villages and hamlets were cut off by mountainous drifts and on the Whitby-Pickering road 150 cars were trapped. All fishing stopped at Bridlington as 70 mph winds pounded the pier. Farmers were advised to shoot invading sparrows to conserve supplies of grain.

January 1963. The A166 Stamford Bridge to Driffield road at the top of Garrowby Hill. (Yorkshire Post Newspapers Ltd)

February 1963. Barges trapped in the ice on the River Hull at Dunswell. (Hull Daily Mail)

By 18th January, Britain had almost been 'cut in half' by the blizzards, the unexpected severity of the conditions taking even women's woollen underwear manufacturers unawares. 'I have had to turn away dozens of orders,' explained the manageress of one outfitters in Doncaster, 'the makers say they have been caught with their pants down!'

It was a similar story on the roads, the national trait of unpreparedness encouraging the usual jibes and comparisons with continental transport authorities. This time, however, the exceptionally harsh conditions crippled even the German communications network and all shipping on the Rhine stopped as their last operating waterway became a ribbon of ice. Back home, the river Hull froze on 19th January and on that terrible day two seamen died in the Humber as a result of an accident in gale force winds and heaving waves which froze as they cascaded over the stricken *Cawood*. Also on 19th January, the wind was so strong at Spurn Point that snow and sand were whipped up

January 1963 – Contemplating the roof of the postman's van on Shaw Ridge, Bransdale. The van was buried after gale force winds drifted moorland snow. (Mr T L Collier)

together in a 'swirling, stinging haze'. Torn from their moorings, Humber lightships and marker buoys were washed out to sea, their absence posing a threat to navigation. Soon, the Ouse and the Humber itself froze, the *Hull Daily Mail* breaking the stark news... 'Humber Is Out Of Action...Last Light Gone... navigation only at extreme risk...ice locked'.

So cold was the weather by February (9.5°F below average) that for the first time since 1881, Hardrow Force, the highest single waterfall in England was almost completely iced up – a solid mountain of ice measuring 70 ft wide and 50 ft high with one spectacular icicle spanning 60 ft. In Halifax, the football league ground was opened as an ice rink and across the North York Moors at Fylingdales Early Warning Station there was the biggest RAF helicopter airlift in history.

'The wind is blowing at between 70 and 80 miles per hour and no one is allowed outside alone,' said Max Goldman, station manager. 'It is too dangerous out there. Conditions are unbelievably bad, worse than anything I have experienced even in Alaska.' Cut off for two days and nights with supplies fast running out, it was decided to evacuate the base and 270 personnel were flown to safety.

In nearby Saltersgate a shepherd's croft was badly damaged in an avalanche, tons of snow smashing down most of the front wall and roof after the worried occupier had moved to safety. On the western wastes, just over the county border near the Snake Pass, a similar accumulation of snow threatened to come crashing down, the Derbyshire County Council using explosives to topple a 30 ft high ice tower.

Throughout the county the cold snap was attended by power cuts to homes and industry and there were scores of lay offs in the building trades. Football fixtures were decimated, one FA Cup day losing 23 of the scheduled 32 games. Problems of frozen water mains led to widespread water shortages, 10,000 homes in Calderdale alone suffering from ruptured pipes. But it was not all gloom. One unexpected consolation of the raw conditions was the availability of cheap sole. According to trawlermen, the continental freeze had encouraged vast shoals of fish to swim to warmer waters off the east coast where they were readily caught for the northern market. 'An ice-up of the shoaling grounds off the Dutch and German coasts has sent them up to 90 miles into the North Sea.'

25th March, 1968 – Pedal Eau, Lincoln Street, York. After heavy rains in the Dales, the Ouse overflowed and inundated hundreds of residential and commercial properties along the river bank. (Press Agency (York) Ltd)

On 14th February, for the first time that year, the Tan Hill Inn, high on the Pennines at an elevation of 1,732 ft, received a paying customer! The landlord's greeting to the gentleman followed the example of a preceding potman, who during a previous freeze-up had saluted a snow-covered shepherd in April with the words, 'Happy New Year!' Cut off since Christmas 1962, the inn had been far from hospitable. Whisky bottles had shattered as a result of the intense cold and the beer had frozen solid.

Although March 1963 temperatures were again below average, the mercury slowly rose during the first part of the month and Yorkshire became green again.

8th September 1965: The Danger of Lightning

Bill Foggitt had a lucky escape that year. Perhaps the weather genie was rancoured at the unfailing accuracy of his weather predictions? Bill recalls:

'The only time my home South Villa was struck by lightning (at least since we came here in 1921) was on September 8th 1965. A lightning flash struck the telephone and blew it up. Fortunately we were all away from home at the time because the electrician who came to repair the telephone told us that anyone standing by it at the time would have been killed.'

2nd July 1968: Hail, Wind . . . and Sand

In an unprecedented midsummer assault, Bradford was struck by a freak storm which caused widespread damage and flooding. Hailstones the size of golf balls peppered the district, bringing down ceilings, smashing windows and greenhouses and reducing vegetable plots to puree. Striking the ground with such force that

Mr and Mrs R Burras of Apperley Bridge, Bradford, digging out their car following the freak hailstorm of 2nd July 1968. (Mr R Burras)

flagstones were pitted and road surfaces crazed, the hailstones accumulated in drifts up to five ft deep. Subsequent flooding was the main problem and the emergency services were at full stretch pumping out cellars and evacuating residents from dangerous buildings.

A potential death trap, the submerged Forster Square subway was bravely searched by police frogman Ronnie Heywood acting on reports of two missing persons. Thankfully, no bodies were found. After rescuing a number of people from the marooned subway kiosk and toilets, the manager of a local newsagent's was praised for his unselfish action. 'He deserves a medal for what he did,' said Mrs Peggy Robinson, who went on to mention another gallant hero. 'My kiosk was surrounded by water up to the counter. Then a young man about 20 came across the kiosk wearing swimming trunks and carried me out on his shoulders. He didn't stop to say who he was...'

Mops were out at the Brown Muffs store and at other shops in the city centre. Industrial premises also suffered. All the electrical machinery at the Universal Containers factory in Apperley Bridge was awash and a three ft pile of hailstones covered the workshop floor.

Odsal Stadium had its share of woes. Flood damage, coming only six weeks before the start of the season, was described as 'a calamity' by club vice-chairman Frank Hillam. Cascading down the terraces, water demolished fences, ripped up embankments and left piles of grit and ash on the pitch. Supporters were urgently asked to help clean up the mess.

Further afield there was extensive flooding in Littletown, and in Cleckheaton enterprising schoolboy canoeists ferried vital provisions to stranded families. In Guiseley, staff at the premises of the Guiseley Engineering Company were swamped in a five ft deep tide and had to be rescued through a skylight.

The massive hailstones stripped bark from fruit trees and completely flattened raspberry canes belonging to businessman Reg Burras of Apperley Bridge. 'My wife rang me at work. It was reasonably warm so she put several specimen hailstones in the fridge as proof. When I got home I found my garden had been pounded to a green mush and I had to dig out my car. Coming through my open garage door the ice had completely encased the central heating boiler, extinguishing the pilot light. I had to chip it away with a pick. When I pressed the ignition button there was a tremendous bang and I was skated clean out of the garage. But for the ice I would have had tremendous grazes.'

Meanwhile, in the Harrogate district, there were more problems. Around 10.45 am blackness descended and the storm tracked south-west and north-east across Haverah Park, Harrogate, Killinghall, Ripley and beyond. Street and headlights were switched on in Harrogate town, and hailstones, some golf ball size, came thundering down. Thousands of windows in homes and greenhouses were smashed – nearly every south-west facing pane in Ripley was broken – leaves were shredded, bark was pitted, the entire local apple crop was lost and herbaceous plants were pulverised. On Killinghall Moor, gorse bushes were mown down by the hail, cornfields were laid waste, swallows were knocked from the sky and there was a heavy mortality amongst pheasants. Some of the birds caught in the open were found 'ready plucked'.

Shortly before mid-day, the persistent beast moved north. Leeming had 1.4 inches of rain in eight and a half minutes. Bill Foggitt remembers it vividly. 'The events of 2nd July were the most dramatic highlights of my 66 year diary. A few folk in the Thirsk area feared that the end of the world had come on that memorable Tuesday. My mother, who was sitting in our front room window facing west called out excitedly, "Come and look at this huge black cloud racing towards us." I was upstairs at the time and scarcely had I reached the window when the great cloud was overhead, turning day into night, pitch black and very cold. Intensifying the darkness came a fierce howling wind which continued long after the blackness had gone. My mother, an enthusiastic weather-watcher and then 86 years old, said she had never experienced anything like it before.

'The darkness lasted for about three minutes and the welcome return to daylight revealed piles of branches from the trees twisted off onto our lawn and the paths around. The episode had been accompanied by a short shower of exceptionally large hailstones, and later we heard that an elderly lady had been killed by a flash of lightning at Northallerton and as the whirlwind crossed the cornfields near Ripon it had severed the ears of corn from the stalks. At Worlds End Bridge, a mile west of my home, at least half a dozen willow trees had been torn asunder. The day previous to the storm had been exceptionally hot in London and the south, and it seemed that the whirlwind had been caused by a clash of warm air blowing in from the south-west and cold air from the north-east.'

It is interesting to note that on that preceding day, heavy rain laden with Saharan sand brought an unexpected bonus for the proprietors of Yorkshire car washes! Several thousand tons of sand were estimated to have fallen on England on that equally memorable Monday.

12th September 1968: 'Hull Waterlogged As 5m Tons Of Rain Fall'

The dramatic report in the *Hull Daily Mail* gave the grim statistics following 27 hours of torrential rain. Three successive electrical storms, described by one eyewitness who viewed the spectacle from the Wolds as 'like a wartime blitz on the city', deluged Pearson Park weather station with 3.59 inches of rain.

Across the town, homes, factories, shops, offices and public houses were all flooded, roads were blocked and electricity supplies interrupted. The streets of Cottingham and the surrounding fields were under three ft of water. At Stackyard Farm, floodwater topped a five-bar gate. 'It was a foot deep in our living room,' said farmer Edward Barrett. 'We have lost two pig litters, all drowned.'

91

20th March 1969: Super Cool

'Arse over apex' is a colourful Yorkshire expression to describe the problems experienced by pedestrians on 20th March. Trapped under a blanket of cold air, water-saturated clouds released their rain which became super-cooled as it fell to earth, striking the ground as glaze. Everything was coated with a slippery film of ice, the dangerous conditions afflicting parts of Sheffield, southern Pennine areas above 400 ft and the Yorkshire Wolds. Freezing on contact, the glaze caused numerous minor falls for pedestrians and scores of collisions for motorists. Encased in accumulated coatings of ice, the Independent Television Company's Emley Moor transmitter, at an elevation of 1,270 ft, collapsed following days of gales and sub-zero temperatures.

28th/29th September 1969: Fish Swim In Hull's Old Town

A freak 33 ft 6 inches tidal surge caused massive flooding in Hull's historic heart. The nearby village of Paull was marooned and thousands of acres of farmland were swamped. On the Humber ten miles upstream, the river gauge showed an all-time high tide of 25 ft 9 inches.

Scores of shops, offices, factories and warehouses in the Old Town were inundated at breakfast time on 29th September. Two electricity transformers caught fire due to water penetration and short circuiting, and Humber ferry sailings were cancelled. Water engulfed the Humber Street Fruit Market in minutes, ruining tons of peas, cauliflowers, apples, pears and other foodstuffs. There was little time for evasive action. 'The water came in so quickly,' said fruit wholesaler Albert Richmor. 'We have had nothing as bad as this since the period between the wars.' Corporation Pier became an island and in the flooded

Fishing from the doorstep of the General Post Office in Hull, 29 September 1969. Fish were actually seen swimming about in the floodwater. (Hull Daily Mail)

Nelson Street premises of the United Towing Company, a stoical Mr Alf Lord declared in lighter vein, 'I caught a fish in our car park, and it was still wriggling!'

There were other unusual sightings. In South Church Side, the non-slip wooden block road surface 'floated like a carpet'. In for

93

Wooden, non-slip setts which made up the road surface in South Church Side, Hull, were dislodged by the force of the floodwaters – 29 September 1969. (Hull Daily Mail)

repair, the damaged tanker *Wheatcroft* rose in the Tower Street Dry Dock, and the Humber banks, like the streets of Hamelin, were filled with rats frantically escaping drowning. Further afield, shipyard workers in Hessle had to climb onto their factory roof for safety, and there were also flood problems in Saltend, Hedon, Kilnsea, Hornsea, Barmston and Bridlington.

Snippets from the Stinging Sixties

1960: Rain fell every day on the Pennines during the month of July. Malham Tarn recorded total precipitation of 9.71 inches. Although Bill Foggitt registered an absolute drought in Thirsk between 16th June and 4th July, the annual rainfall tally for the district was an exceptional 31.68 inches.

*On the A170 at the summit of the notorious Sutton Bank near Thirsk,
25th November, 1969. (Press Agency (York) Ltd)*

A 'snow coach' on the B1363 at Brandsby, 25th November, 1969. (Press Agency (York) Ltd)

1962: Ten ft of cliff collapsed at Aldborough during November.

1964: On 18th July, Nidderdale experienced violent thunderstorms. Hailstones up to one inch in diameter stripped leaves off trees. Torrential rain flushed the hailstones into heaps, some over one ft high.

1965: Wakefield and Whitby sweltered in a temperature of 77°F on 29th March.

Weekend sport on Ilkley Tarn, 1965. (Wharfedale Newspapers)

Wind destroyed No 2A cooling tower at Ferrybridge 'C' Power Station on 1st November.

Heavy rain on 9th December combined with thawing snow to bring extensive flooding to Pateley Bridge. Many roads in the Nidd valley were blocked.

1967: The name of Huddersfield entered the Guinness Book of Records, the town having had the dubious distinction of suffering a record 38 thundery days during the year.

THE WEATHER
IN THE SEVENTIES

26th September 1971: Tornado!

Around four o'clock in the afternoon several startled Rotherham residents gawped at an oncoming 'ice-cream cornet shaped cloud'. The tornado, with a track estimated to be around twelve miles long, damaged houses in Rawmarsh. It was also reported that an Alsatian dog, complete with kennel, was carried over a fence and a garden, and that metal railings were sucked from the ground.

1976: The Great Drought

Few natural phenomena in recent years have had such a profound and long lasting impact on public opinion as the blazing summer of 1976. A truly national event which fuelled the emerging public debate about rain forest exploitation, emissions reductions, global warming, ozone depletion, acid rain and the use of CFCs, the Great Drought will long be remembered as the most compelling argument yet for conservation.

The worst drought in England since 1720 was preceded by a dry and chilly April. In May, rain washed out the Temple Newsam Dog Show in Leeds and the British Hang Gliding Championships in the Hole of Horcum. Bank Holiday roads were quiet, and although Yorkshire water stocks were low, there was no cause for alarm. Four months on, it was an altogether different story, the *Yorkshire Evening Post* recording that 'Britain has turned into a dried out piece of brown sacking, withering under a relentless tropical sun.'

With no appreciable rain having fallen for weeks, by early June the water authorities were signalling concern. There was talk about the need for the conservation of stocks, Mr Alan Bland of Harrogate suggesting a novel method for preserving supplies. 'It is so simple it is laughable,' he wrote in the local press, 'but nobody seems to want to know. Basically the idea is to drill a hole down the centre of the toilet cistern spindle and another in the siphon. This will stop the water rising above a certain level.' Similar action was being recommended in the national newspapers. They advocated the use of bricks in toilet cisterns and they encouraged the sharing of baths with friends!

By 25th June, Centre Court temperatures at Wimbledon had reached 106°F. On the following day the mercury nudged 90°F in Leeds and hundreds of people suffering from heat stroke were attended by the St John's Ambulance Brigade in Bradford, Huddersfield and Wakefield. Cereal crops in the south and east of the region were beginning to wilt, pasture land was being progressively shrivelled up leading to reduced milk yields, and a spontaneous grass fire on the tinder-dry Bellerby Ranges near Bellerby had taken hold. Swimmers and holidaymakers basked in the heat and entrepreneurs made hay whilst the sun shone. Ben Shaws, the soft drinks manufacturer of Huddersfield, increased production by 100% to cater for the unprecedented demand and ice-cream producers in Bridlington sold over one ton of tubs and cones.

On the nation's roads, it was estimated by the RAC that on 27th June, eight million drivers were en route to the resorts. Parts of the M1 near Horbury Lagoon in Wakefield began to crack, another giant moor fire erupted at Wheeldale Moor between Pickering and Whitby, and hundreds of swooning office and factory workers left for home. 'It must have been approaching 100 degrees or more in there,' said one of the 100 workers to quit the David Brown Tractor Factory at Meltham. 'We just could not stand it any longer.' Machinists at the John Naylor clothing plant in Barnsley followed suit and in Bradford's No 1 Crown Court a sympathetic judge, Gilbert Hartley gave permission for members of the bar to remove their wigs and waistcoats!

By July, hosepipe bans were in force across the region and thousands of standpipes were readied for deployment. As the British Oxygen Company made plans to pump life-giving oxygen to fish in the river Wharfe at Tadcaster, the Cabinet was placed on a 'war footing' in anticipation of declaring 'drought areas' all over Britain.

Anxious citizens listened attentively to radio broadcasts and they scanned newspaper forecasts hoping for the promise of rain. The Archbishop of York was asked to pray for the miracle of dark skies, and the Lord relented on 12th July when a deluge visited Bradford. It was not all good news. There was flooding in parts of the city and two golfers had an alarming experience when they were struck by lightning. Mr John Winter and Mr Richard Lupton were knocked to the ground and had their clothes ripped from their bodies by a bolt of lightning that first struck an umbrella. 'Their clothing right down to their socks and underpants was ripped,' said a fellow golfer.

During August there was almost dawn to dusk sunshine for the entire month. Dessicated gardens and fields cracked and cereal and vegetable yields were much reduced, causing price rises. With the heat came explosions in insect populations, the abiding

100

memory for some being the sight of millions of ladybirds gorging on the super-abundant hatches of greenfly.

With reservoir levels falling alarmingly, the water authorities sought to extract ever more water from the rivers. An extra five million gallons per day was siphoned from the river Nidd on top of the nine million gallons previously allowed. Such was the scale of abstraction that some experts believed that unless the operation was curtailed the river would be completely dry by October.

'Scanning the disc of the setting sun during the last week of August 1976,' wrote Bill Foggitt, 'I noticed a conspicuous spot to the right of its centre, the first for several months. I took this to be a sign of the approaching end of the long drought – the longest in Europe for 250 years.'

The famous summer came to an abrupt end by the end of August and ironically, the month of September was the second wettest in England since 1727. Nowhere was the change in the weather more noticable than in the village of Stokesley.

Five ft of water on the 12th September, the worst soaking in the locality for 25 years, caused the river Leven to burst its banks. The tide rushed down Stokesley High Street, flooding houses and shops and terraced homes in Levenside. Fuming at the lack of adequate flood protection, residents condemned the River Board as two policemen, PC Fred Pearson and PC Ian Burkes, donned frogmen's suits to assist in the rescue work. The waters ruined parcels and mail in Mr Pat Annis's post office. 'It had been raining continuously for the previous twelve hours,' explained Mr Annis, 'but I never expected to wake up and find the village under water.'

'My mother', recalls Bill Foggitt, 'who was so well versed in weather lore, remarked during the torrential downpours of

Top and bottom: Floodwaters in Stokesley High Street, 12th September 1976. The rescuers in frogmen's suits are P.C. Fred Pearson and P.C. Ian Burkes. (Press Agency (York) Ltd)

September 1976, "Much water in Autumn, much ice by Christmas." Even though we didn't start greasing our skates straight away, events proved her correct, with November, December and January considerably colder than average, and air frost on Christmas Eve and night. There was no need to take records to guess how much rain we had in the soaking autumn of 1976, because in mid-October, when I travelled from Thirsk to the Lake District by car, it rained heavily all day and we had to motor through deep floods on the Wensleydale roads.'

April 1977: 'Sandstorm Blitz In Wentbridge'

Fierce winds blew swirling clouds of topsoil over the village of Wentbridge. Mrs J. Horn of Moor Lane complained, 'All the hedges have been taken from the fields and the wind is blowing soil across the village. It looks just like a fog and you cannot go out without protecting your face.' A neighbour, Mrs L. Job joined in. 'It was absolutely terrible. There were six inches of dust on the window ledges inside the house and in the hall, and in the kitchen there was a layer of grit over everything.'

1979: Operation Siberia

A little too much Yorkshire stingo can cloud even a weather prophet's judgement! 'I was motoring with friends on New Year's Eve,' explains Bill Foggitt, 'and we became stuck in a snow drift and had to have assistance from passing motorists to get us out!'

The following month of January was one of the coldest in the Foggitt family record books but it was the month of February, when the West Yorkshire police set up 'Operation Siberia', that will go down in history.

Raging blizzards on 15th February brought the whole of Yorkshire to a standstill. Even troops equipped with Scorpion tracked vehicles were defeated by the conditions. Enlisted by the electricity board to ferry engineers to the remote settlement of Hurst in Arkengarthdale, they battled with 20 ft deep snow drifts before admitting defeat. Country roads and motorways alike were impassable. There were 30 ft deep drifts alongside the A1. The A59 Skipton to Harrogate road, the A1079 York to Beverley road and scores of other highways were blocked and all road and rail links between Yorkshire and Lancashire were cut. Thousands of commuters were stranded. Railway stations, hotel corridors and function rooms, and unlikely accommodation like Halifax Town Hall became makeshift dormitories. But it was the Hartshead Moor service station on the M62 that provided the most vital service of all.

In the worst conditions imaginable, 200 drivers made their way to the station, leaving behind lines of abandoned vehicles, stretching nose to tail for half a mile along two carriageways. Assisted by motorway patrol officers, the drivers, some of whom had been trapped in their cabs for five hours, spent the night thawing out and discussing their ordeal which the newspapers subsequently dubbed 'The Battle of Hartshead Moor'.

The harsh conditions were particularly bad in South Yorkshire where a state of emergency was declared on 16th January. The 'Minister for Snow', Denis Howell flew into Sheffield to assess the situation, discovering some of the most chaotic problems in the country.

Successive blizzards hampered relief efforts and attempts to restore communications. Pontefract and Castleford had some of the heaviest snowfalls and in the countryside, diminishing stocks of fuel and food made rescue vital. On 22nd February, troops using Scorpion vehicles battled through the snow to reach the Middleton family in their isolated home at Camhouse Farm,

Buckden. Robert Middleton, his wife and three children had been trapped since Christmas. 'We expect to be cut off during the winter up here,' said Mrs Middleton, 'but it has never been for this long.' Hannah Hauxwell, who had lived alone for 18 years in her remote farmhouse in Baldersdale, County Durham, echoed the sentiments. 'This is the worst winter I have ever experienced.'

30th March, 1979 – the Derwent bursts its banks at Stamford Bridge. (The Swordsman Inn on the left has a number of plaques on the bar marking flood heights.) (Press Agency (York) Ltd)

Seventies Synopsis

1970: The long dry summer had a marked effect on Yorkshire rivers. The rain-fed Aire was well below its normal level. Much reduced flows in the higher reaches encouraged an abundance of weeds and hideous rafts of slime added to the anglers' nightmare. On 16th October, Bill Foggitt enjoyed a spectacular auroral display between the hours of 7 and 8 pm.

1973: Harbingers of bad weather, fieldfares arrived in Yorkshire with an east wind on 11th October. On the following day, Helvellyn and the neighbouring peaks in the Lake District were covered in snow.

1975: The 2nd of June was the most wintery since 1888 and the coldest of the century in the Foggitt journals. Snow fell at Thirkleby near Thirsk. Climbing parties in the Cairngorms reported Arctic conditions with up to seven inches of snow.

1979: On 13th June a large, slow moving cumulonimbus cloud produced a severe storm at Skipton-on-Swale. At Embsay Moor, 2.1 inches of rain fell in just 53 minutes. The following day, Bill Foggitt witnessed the most violent and the longest thunderstorm in his experience. 'It lasted from about 10 am to early evening without a break and with prolonged torrential rain.'

THE WEATHER
IN THE EIGHTIES

July 1980: Hair Raising Adventure At Sea

With conditions set fair, a party of fishermen left Whitby harbour hoping for an uneventful day. They reached the fishing grounds and anchored in a flat calm, little knowing that an amazing experience awaited them. Suddenly, scalps tingled and the hair on a dozen heads stood to attention. Highly perplexed the fishermen wondered what could have caused the phenomenon. The answer came in a flash. Lightning struck the sea near the boat and their hair instantly returned to normal.

An onshore explanation relegated thoughts of spells and sea witches. The atmosphere is invested with what is termed an 'electric field gradient,' charged with between 120 to 150 volts per vertical metre. At ground or sea level the force is negative. Immediately preceding storm activity, voltages are dramatically increased and human hair fibres are very receptive conductors ... QED.

9th July 1984: Fiery Reprimand –
Lightning Strikes York Minster

'York Minster is ablaze!' The stark announcement flashed across the airwaves of a stunned nation. According to some, the

Tornado! A chance sighting by York resident Mr Tony Perry on 26 July 1980. Returning from a business trip Mr Perry crossed the M62 near Goole in his car. Seeing this scene from 'The Wizard of Oz' he pulled over and rattled off eight frames in quick succession. Soon afterwards there was a tremendous storm. Torrential rain and hailstones poured down. The tornado passed over open farmland and there were no reports of damage.

lightning strike was an act of divine rebuke for the heretical comments about the Virgin birth by the outspoken Bishop of Durham. Just three days earlier, the controversial Professor David Jenkins had been consecrated in the Minster amid scenes of unprecedented hostility.

The thunderbolt struck around 2.30 am. According to eyewitnesses, lightning had played around the great structure for some time. 'It was a spectacular and breathtaking sight and I saw several lightning bolts falling very near the cathedral,' said Mr Ewan Porter, whose friends witnessed the actual incident from their hostel window. The prelude to the strike – a low-powered

Top: York Minster in flames — the scene from Stonegate in the early hours of 9 July 1984. (York & County Press)
Bottom: The morning after the terrible night before... The Archbishop of Canterbury, Dr Robert Runcie, surveys the scenes of devastation. (York & County Press)

electrical discharge known as corona – was followed by two devastating bolts of energy, one of which melted the lightning conductor. 'Lightning has a very large current of about 10,000 amps,' said an expert. 'Corona very often happens just before lightning and causes no noise except for a slight hissing sound, rather like high tension power cables in wet weather.'

The south transept took the full impact. Fanned by a stiff breeze the whole roof was soon consumed in flames and molten lead began to cascade from the timbers even before the fire brigade arrived. The brigade quickly tackled the blaze, described by the officer commanding as being like a giant Roman candle. Within three hours, the fire had been brought under control, but the ceiling of the transept and the priceless Rose Window had collapsed in ruins. Visitors openly wept at the sight. Dr Runcie [the then Archbishop of Canterbury] affirmed, 'It will rise again.'

26th April 1986: Radioactive Rain

Unannounced to the world, the nuclear catastrophe at Chernobyl released a radioactive cloud that contaminated half of Europe. Carried on the prevailing winds, some of the deadly material washed to earth in raindrops, polluting much of Scotland and England. Despite initial assurances from the authorities that the risks to health were negligible, tests by the National Radiological Protection Board found that radioactive contaminants in ground samples were up to ten times higher in the north of England than in the south. People in Yorkshire were warned not to drink rainwater, there was constant monitoring of milk and some farmers were banned from sending carcases to market.

16th October 1987: The Great Storm

Comforted by the reassuring words of weatherman Michael Fish, the nation slept soundly. Data from weather ships, satellites, batteries of probes, hundreds of computers and thousands of weathermen concurred that winds in the following 24 hours would be light. Was this the most misleading weather forecast in meteorological history? Yes! Enter the Great Storm!

Brewing out in the English Channel, the storm changed track and hit southern England in the early hours of the morning catching everyone unawares. Exceeding 100 mph in places, the winds left scores of people dead, hundreds of homes demolished and cars and boats smashed to smithereens. Communications were crippled and millions of trees were felled changing the geography of several counties, the storm leaving in its wake insurance claims estimated at £1 billion.

With communal sighs of relief almost as palpable as the storm itself, the winds abated over Yorkshire and passed out into the North Sea. There was only minor damage and disruption in the county. The wind was vicious on the coast and coastguards warned seafarers that they would be 'committing suicide' by putting to sea. There was some damage to properties in Pinfold Lane, South Cave and localised flooding in Wakefield and Huddersfield, but apart from that Yorkshire emerged generally unscathed.

January 1987: White-out

'The mild winter will come to a sudden end this week,' warned the *Yorkshire Post* on 6th January. In anticipation of the cold, readers turfed out long-johns and bought in supplies of anti-freeze and prepared for the worst. And it was the worst. By 11th January, the temperature across the county had plunged to

– 6°C – the coldest for 30 years – dropping to an all time low in South and West Yorkshire during the following night.

On 12th January, the thermometer in Sheffield never rose above – 6.1°C, the coldest day since records began in 1882. Accompanying the cold, blizzards paralysed large parts of Yorkshire. On the M62 dozens of lorries were stranded after diesel fuel froze solid in their tanks. The A66 Scotch Corner to Penrith route was closed and conditions on the A1 and M1 were described by the police as 'a white out'.

With renewed intensity on the unlucky 13th January, snow storms again swept the county. Drifting snow isolated Withernsea, the A58 Sowerby to Rochdale road was impassable; an 81 year old man in York died of hypothermia following a fuse blow-out in his home; and in Huddersfield an 84 year old lady froze to death. West Yorkshire Fire Brigade warned householders not to use lighted candles in bathrooms in attempting to prevent frozen pipes. This followed the experience of one Huddersfield couple whose precautionary flame set fire to an acrylic bath and burnt down their house. At the Flamingo Land Zoo near Pickering, concerned staff had to take 120 Cuban and Chilean pink flamingoes for walks to stop their legs from seizing up.

Schools closed across the region and by 14th January, with yet more snow, the situation on the Trans-Pennine motorway got even worse, over 1,000 vehicles being abandoned in a Siberian blizzard. 'Unless you were there,' said one lorry driver, 'you cannot imagine what it was like. Driving conditions were atrocious.'

There were crumbs of comfort from foreign correspondents in Russia and Norway. In Leningrad, the temperature fell to – 31°F. 'Never in the annals of the Leningrad weather service – and meteorologists have been working here since 1743 – have such low temperatures been registered for several days running,' said a spokesman. And Norwegian doctors warned people against drinking hot beverages immediately after coming in from the cold. Several incidents of cracking tooth enamel had been reported!

Back home, the RAF and the army assisted the emergency services in ferrying patients to hospitals and in breaking the snow blockade of isolated communities. British Gas called out the Royal Irish Rangers. Their all-terrain vehicles crashed through the snow drifts to deliver gas engineers to Withernsea. Children playing at the roadside waved excitedly as the mini convoy of Snowcats passed them. A local resident, Mrs Pat Parker was stunned at the efforts invested in repairing her central heating boiler.

Thankfully, the harsh conditions petered out and a thaw set in just as British Rail sent its Bielhack self-propelled rotary snow blower to England from its Inverness base.

Snippets from the Erratic Eighties

1982: The A1 at Leeming Bar was covered with ten inches of water as a consequence of 47 hours of continual rain.

1983: Exceptionally high tides almost 20 ft above normal caused flooding in Filey and Scarborough. Force nine and ten gales off Hull played havoc with shipping.

1985: Two inches of snow fell on Buckden Pike on 8th June. Bill Foggitt confounded experts who predicted an Arctic winter. Temperatures lifted, confirming forecasts based on observations of flowering jasmine and increased mole activity.

A waterspout (maritime tornado) photographed in March 1989 off Kettleness near Whitby. (H Mayfield)

1986: Over two inches of rain fell in Nidderdale between 14th and 17th April. Many roads were flooded and hundreds of lambs and ewes drowned. Wildfowl nesting at Gouthwaite reservoir were washed out.

1986: On 1st July, lightning hit signalling systems on British Rail's main east coast line and there were 90 minute delays at Tollerton between York and Thirsk.

INTO THE
NINETIES

25th January 1990: It Happened Again!

According to the meteorological law of averages, a storm of the magnitude of that inflicted on southern England in October 1987 was unlikely to visit these shores again for another 250 years. Some law! Less than three years were to elapse before capricious Mother Nature was at it again. But this storm differed from its predecessor in several important respects. Firstly it struck during daylight hours when the population was most vulnerable. Secondly, it was predicted, and thirdly, of vital significance to Yorkshire folk, it travelled north.

An Atlantic depression, deepening explosively as it swept in from the east coast of America, was tracked by the Meteorological Office and prime time warnings were given by the BBC. Yorkshire braced itself for the shock. It came as predicted, winds up to 100 mph sweeping the county. There were a number of fatalities, contributing to the national death toll of 47. In Keighley a woman was blown off her moped under the wheels of an oncoming car on the A629 and on Saddleworth Moor a 16 year old youth was killed when he was blown into a swollen stream.

Hundreds of minor casualties, the result of flying debris, falling masonry and snapped-off branches and trees, were treated in local hospitals. There were chaotic scenes on the roads. Scores of overturned vehicles littered highways in North Yorkshire, two lorries were blown over the Humber Bridge and after a spate of accidents in South Yorkshire, police issued a plea to motorists to avoid the Tinsley Viaduct 'like the plague'. Rail services were badly disrupted, Hull's main arteries all being closed after winds ripped down power lines.

Structural damage was widespread and the emergency services were at full stretch coping with a welter of calls. The gale ripped off the aluminium roof of the Irish Centre in Leeds trapping nearby residents in their houses. On the Orchard Park estate in Hull, corrugated iron roofing was torn from garages and in the north of the city, a pigeon loft was tossed into the Barmston Drain with 45 birds still inside.

As the storm subsided the nauseous whine of chain-saws could be heard in hundreds of locations. Across Britain an astounding four million trees were felled, a number which pales into insignificance when compared with the astronomical figures quantifying the cost of the hurricane in pounds sterling. It is estimated that the storm led to insurance claims in excess of £2,000 million.

1990: The Greenhouse Effect?

On 30th April the *Yorkshire Post* noted, 'Leeds was the warmest place in Britain yesterday as April beamed into the record books becoming the sunniest since records began more than 60 years ago.' April was in fact one of the driest in the Foggitt journals. Measurable rainfall amounted to a mere 0.3 inches.

On 2nd August, Harrogate recorded its highest ever temperature – 91.5°F August temperatures nationally were amongst the highest recorded since 1659.

February 1991: 'One Steppe From Siberia'

They blamed it on the Russians. Cold air swept in from the central plains bringing chaos to Yorkshire.

All parts of the county were covered in a thick blanket of snow. The Dales had 15.7 inches. The fall in Bingley measured a staggering 18.5 inches – the deepest in the country. On 8th February, east coast rail services between King's Cross and Edinburgh were cut by 50% and motor traffic slowed to a crawl on the Trans-Pennine M62. Dales, Wolds and North York Moors routes were similarly affected, hundreds of abandoned vehicles adding to the problems.

With temperatures down to − 25°C, a jarring experience after two consecutive mild winters, there was much hardship, especially amongst pensioners. The Government were warned that hundreds of old folk would die unless supplementary cold weather payments were made, and, although the Cabinet were obdurate to the pleas, local councils and voluntary agencies responded by offering practical help and advice. In Sheffield, an emergency hot line was set up and in Bridlington, people were asked to 'adopt an elderly person during the current bout of bad weather'.

Dozens of schools closed in Calderdale, Sheffield, Doncaster, North Yorkshire and Humberside, and transport authorities exhausted winter maintenance funds in their desperate round-the-clock battles with snow and ice.

The lasting memory of this famous winter was yet another 'verbal pearler' from British Rail. In trying to defend the failure of their £1 million high-tech Class 91 locomotives which ground to an ignominious halt during the blizzards, they explained . . . 'It was the wrong type of snow!' Apparently the fine powdery snow could not be prevented from blowing through filters protecting high voltage electrical components and the engines seized up. The Transport Secretary was not amused. 'It is a matter of some very considerable concern that brand new rolling stock, very recently introduced, should be incapable of dealing with the sorts of circumstances we have seen during the last few days'.

1991: Ouse At Hundred Year High

In a year that was to see a remarkably low tally of sunshine − 300 hours less than average and the lowest since records began in 1924 in the Harrogate district − the Ouse reached its highest

Cars push their way steadily through flooded Skeldergate, York − 24 February 1991. (Mr M Barritt)

Top: Kings Staith from Ouse Bridge – 24 February 1991. (Mr M Barritt)

Bottom: Ouse Bridge, York, from Peckitt Street on 24 February 1991. (Mr M Barritt)

24th February, 1991 – Army reinforcements were called to assist the fire brigade in evacuating stranded residents from their flooded homes after the River Ure burst its banks in Boroughbridge. (Press Agency (York) Ltd)

level for a century. On 25th February, melting snow and heavy rain across the region brought severe flooding. The river Wharfe burst its banks between Addingham and Pool-in-Wharfedale, drivers in York were diverted away from the flooded city centre, and, following a National Rivers Authority red alert, about 30 families were threatened with evacuation in Otley. 'I was born here more than 70 years ago,' said Otley town councillor Norman Hindle of Bridge Avenue, 'and on Saturday it was the biggest river I have ever seen.' Downstream, in the tap room of the long suffering King's Arms in York, another flood marker plaque was readied to join its cousins on the bar.

This drab year was noted for a fine display of the Northern Lights, seen from Harrogate on 8th November.

1992: Miserable August Blamed On Volcano

Scarborough landladies had to blame something for the drop in takings during the normally sunny holiday month of August. So the admonishing rolling pin was pointed at Mount Pinatubo in the Phillipines!

A series of volcanic eruptions from Pinatubo in June 1991 spewed a 3,000 mile long shroud of sulphur dioxide and ash into the atmosphere, scientists from the National Aeronautical Space Administration in New York concluding that global temperatures and hours of surface sunlight had been significantly reduced by the absorbing effects of the cloud. Statistics proved, assured NASA, that six to 18 months after volcanic activity, eastern American states and most of north-western Europe had bad summers. But there was some consolation. Pinatubo's eruption was but a tantrum compared with the explosion of Toba in Sumatra 73,500 years ago. Five times as big a bang as Pinatubo's, its eruption is reckoned by some to have caused the last Ice Age.

September 1992: Goodness Gracious, Great Balls of Fire!

Just before midnight, pensioner Mrs E. Jackson of Goole Grange Cottages, Goole, was awakened by a strange pulsating glow. Pulling back her curtains, she discovered two incandescent balls of light as large as a house, hovering over the distant fields. This rarely witnessed phenomenon of ball lightning persisted for 15 minutes then disappeared.

21st December 1992: Fog Mayhem

Sickeningly repetitive, the catalogue of annual motorway accidents continued in a month noted for black ice and thick fog. The M62 near Huddersfield was closed after a 60 vehicle pile up. One person was killed and 60 injured. Further south on the A1 between Knottingley and Wentbridge, there was a second fatality and 13 injuries resulting from a string of multiple accidents and on the A1 near Doncaster, one person died and 26 were injured following a 50 vehicle pile up which closed both road carriageways over a distance of 20 miles.

Although visibility was down to a few yards, irresponsible drivers failed to reduce speeds. Chief Inspector Mel Bunting of the West Yorkshire Police said, 'I don't think drivers are learning. We keep asking people to drive slowly and I don't think many of them know what slow is . . . It is no less than criminal behaviour in some cases.'

On the west-bound carriageway of the M62, a motorist, Mrs Jean Goodhead from Castleford echoed the complaint. 'It has almost made me want to give up driving. I was more scared of the other motorists flying past me and behind me than the weather.'

4th January 1993: First Snow Of Winter Brings Train Chaos To Leeds

Once again the weather caught British Rail napping. After successive fiascos blamed on troublesome leaves and the 'wrong type of snow', this time it was a vain attempt at thawing frozen points. With only a dusting of snow in the suburbs, exasperated commuters faced long delays and sat in motionless trains. A British Rail spokeswoman explained, 'Not very much is moving in and out of Leeds. It is a very difficult situation which we are trying to rectify. We have launched a full inquiry as to why, when we have contingency plans, things can be so grim.'

1993: Spring Has Sprung A Leak

The combined effects of spring rain and melting snow in the Yorkshire Dales caused the Ouse to burst its banks on 15th May. The river rose rapidly to twelve ft above its normal level, and although riverside roads, walkways and some commercial premises (including the King's Arms – again!) were flooded, recently completed flood containment works protected many homes.

After a scorching interlude of five days in early June, there was more heavy rain. On the 9th, Sheffield commuters were badly affected by flooding on Abbeydale Road, Beauchief, and rail passengers travelling between Shipley and Bradford suffered long delays after lightning struck a signal box. There were yet more floods on 11th June. As 'the storm of the century' hit west Wales, driving 500 Llandudno residents from their homes, persistent downpours, particularly in South Yorkshire, led to a rash of 999 calls from householders with flooded cellars. The river Sheaf in Sheffield overflowed and two motorists in London Road at Heeley Bridge had to scramble to safety through their car sunroofs to avoid a seven ft deep torrent.

Goodbye to all that – Ken Archer, an engineer based at Holme Moss in the mid 1950s, was glad to leave behind 'the most diabolical winter, when we walked up from Holme village in appalling weather, in the teeth of driving wind and snow'.

Glossary of Common Weather Terms

Altitude: Height above sea level.

Anticyclone: An area of high pressure bringing fine weather.

Atmosphere: A gaseous envelope surrounding the earth.

Aurora borealis: The 'Northern Lights', a spectacular heavenly phenomenon producing brilliant displays of colour, caused by the atmospheric disturbance of oxygen and nitrogen by electrons and protons radiating from the sun.

Ball lightning: A suspended sphere of radiating energy explained as an electrical dust cloud, a slow burning admixture of air and carbon or an ionised mass of gas.

Barometer: An instrument for measuring atmospheric pressure.

Clouds: Condensed water vapour.

Drought: A prolonged absence of precipitation.

Fog: Clouds of condensing water vapour resulting from the interaction of warm and cold air.

Front: The boundary between two masses of air of differing densities or temperatures.

Frost: Frozen dew or water vapour.

Gale: Wind measured in velocity between 34 and 40 knots.

Glaze: Rain which freezes on contact with the ground.

Hail: A form of precipitation consisting of ice pellets of more than 1 cm (0.39 inches) in diameter.

Hurricane: Wind measured in velocity in excess of 64 knots.

Lightning: A flash of energy produced by an electrical discharge between clouds or between clouds and the ground.

Mist: An increase in water droplet concentrations in the air resulting in decreased visibility.

Rain: Liquid precipitation whose individual droplets measure up to 6 mm (0.24 inches in diameter).

Rainbow: Optical phenomena occuring when sunlight is refracted into spectral colours by shower clouds. The larger the raindrops, the more intense the rainbow.

Sleet: Form of precipitation consisting of a mixture of melting snow and rain.

Snow: Frozen flakes of ice in the shape of six-pointed stars.

Thermometer: Instrument for measuring temperature.

Thunder: The audible consequences of air particle compression and collision in air vacuums created by lightning activity.

Thunderstorm: Onset of rapidly rising moist air attended by heavy rain, thunder and lightning.

Tornado: A violent columnar spiral of wind travelling at great speed.

Wind: The process of pressure equalisation: air moving from high pressure to low pressure.

Acknowledgements

Bill Foggitt and I would like to thank most sincerely all those Yorkshire people, some no longer living in the county, who replied to my requests via local newspapers for pictorial memories of weather incidents from the past. Space has not permitted the use of all of them but I am nonetheless grateful for the trouble taken to show me the many scenes of snow, flood and local chaos.

L.M.

Index

Aberford 25
Acaster Malbis 56
Addingham 120
Aire, river 66, 75, 106
Aldborough 96
Apperley Bridge 89
Arkengarthdale 104

Baldersdale 105
Barden 44
Barlby 66, 68
Barmston 94, 116
Barnoldswick 61
Barnsley 100
Batley 23
Beauchief 123
Bellerby 99
Bellerby Ranges 99
Bentley 53, 69
Beverley 104
Bingley 117
Black Hambleton 57
Blacktoft 40, 64
Blaxton 55
Boroughbridge 46, 120
Bradford 79, 87, 88, 99, 100, 123
Bramham 80
Brandsby 96
Bransdale 84
Bridlington 54, 57, 73, 82, 94, 99, 117
Briggswath 50-51
Brightside 35
Buckden 61, 105, 113
Burnsall 40, 44

Calderdale 86, 117
Castle Bolton 41
Castleford 62, 68, 104, 122
Castleton 48, 53
Cleckheaton 89
Cliffe 68
Cod Beck 53
Cottingham 91
Cracoe Fell 44
Cross Fell 40, 72, 77

Damflask 35
Danby 48, 53
Dent 62
Derwent, river 51, 66, 105
Dishworth 56
Don, river 40, 53, 66
Doncaster 81, 83, 117, 122
Driffield 82
Dunford Bridge 58
Dunswell 84

Easby 40
Egton 53
Eglon Bridge 48
Embsay 44, 61
Embsay Moor 106
Emley Moor 92
Esk, river 48, 51
Eskdale 51

Ferrybridge 81, 97
Filey 41, 113
Filey Brig 41
Finningley 55, 73
Flamborough Head 13, 18, 39, 41, 74, 82
Fylingdales 85

Glaisdale 53
Goole 81, 121
Gouthwaite 114
Gowdall 68, 69
Great Ayton 40
Grosmont 53
Guisborough 47
Guiseley 89

Halifax 85, 104
Hardraw Force 85
Harewood 80
Harrogate 53, 80, 90, 99, 104, 117, 118, 120
Hartshead Moor 104
Haverah Park 90

Hedon 94
Heeley Bridge 123
Helmsley 22
Hemingborough 68
Hessle 94
Hole of Horcum 99
Holme Moss 78, 124
Holmfirth 22, 29-30, 72, 76
Holmpton 14, 16
Hook Moor 25
Hopperton 57
Hornsea 73, 94
Hornsea Beck 15
Hornsey 15
Howden 47
Hubberholme 61
Huddersfield 39, 65, 81, 97, 99, 111, 112, 122
Huggate 62
Hull 22, 39, 62, 64, 72, 73, 75, 77, 91-94, 113, 116
Hull, river 83
Humber, river 15, 29, 64, 69, 83, 85, 92
Humber Bridge 116
Hunsingore 57
Hurst 104
Huskar 27-28
Hutton le Hole 59

Ilkley 43, 60, 64, 73, 74, 97

Keighley 115
Kettleness 114
Kettlewell 22
Kildale 40
Kildwick 39
Killingholme 41
Killinghall 90
Killinghall Moor 90
Kilnsea 15, 28, 33-34, 94
Kings Straithe 119
Kirkbymoorside 59
Knottingley 25, 81, 122

Langstrothdale 61
Lealholm 53
Leeds 60, 61, 62, 65,
  73, 74, 77, 78, 79, 80,
  81, 98, 99, 116,
  122-123
Leeming Bar 90, 113
Leven 101
Leyburn 47
Lindholm 69
Linton on Ouse 56, 57,
  59
Littletown 89
Lofthouse Moor 62
Low Bradfield 35
Lumb Clough Bridge 45

Malham Tarn 78, 94
Malinbridge 35
Meltham 100
Mexborough 61
Micklefield 25
Murton Common 57

Newhay 68
Nidd 97, 101
Nidderdale 62, 82, 97,
  114
Normanton 61
Northallerton 91
North York Moors 53,
  85, 117
Nunthorpe 57

Osmotherley 57, 76
Otley 80, 120
Ouse 21, 22, 40, 56, 66,
  118, 120, 123
Ouse Bridge 21
Owthorne 15

Pateley Bridge 6, 97
Paull 92
Penistone 25, 52
Pennines 87
Pickering 82, 100, 112
Pontefract 72, 104
Pool-in-Wharfedale 120
Preston 41

Ravenser Odd 15

Rawmarsh 98
Ribblehead 62
Riccall 68
Ripley 90
Riplingham 82
Ripon 46, 47, 78, 91
Rivelin valley 35
Rochdale 112
Rotherham 80, 98
Rudding 80
Ruswarp 48, 50-51,
  53
Rye, river 66

Saddleworth Moor 115
Saltersgate 85
Saltend 94
Scarborough 18-19, 20,
  30-33, 46, 47, 54, 72,
  80, 113, 121
Scammonden 76
Scotch Corner 112
Selby 39, 66, 67, 68, 70,
  71
Sharlston 66
Sheffield 35-37, 40, 42,
  46, 47, 60, 62, 63, 72,
  79, 80, 92, 104, 112,
  117, 123
Shipley 123
Shipton-by-Beningborough
  56
Silkstone 27-28
Silsden 45, 75
Skeffling 15
Skeldergate 118
Skipton 44-45, 61, 62,
  104
Skipton on Swale
  106
Slaithwaite 76
Sleights 48, 50, 53
Snaith 68
Sowerby 112
Spurn Point 13, 15, 17,
  18, 29, 72, 73, 83
Stamford Bridge 51, 82,
  105
Starbotton 22
Stean Moor 62
Stirton with Thorlby 44

Stokesley 101, 102
Sutton Bank 52, 54
Swale 66
Swanland 42
Swine 64

Tadcaster 20, 22, 100
Thirkleby 106
Thirsk 9-11, 22, 38, 40,
  41, 53, 60, 87, 90, 94,
  95, 103, 114
Thixendale 60, 82
Thorpe Fell 44
Thorlby 62
Thorne 69
Tinsley 42, 116
Tollerton 114
Towton Moor 20-21

Upperthong 76
Ure, river 46, 78,
  120

Wakefield 39, 45, 47,
  62, 81, 96, 99, 100,
  111
Wentbridge 103, 122
Wensleydale 9, 41,
  103
Wetherby 65
Wharfe 54, 64, 65, 66,
  100, 120
Wharfedale 43
Wheeldale Moor 100
Whernside 56
Whitby 22, 32, 34, 40,
  41, 48, 49, 51, 53, 80,
  82, 96, 100, 107, 114
Wistow 68, 69
Withernsea 18, 73, 112,
  113
Wold Newton 54
Worlds End Bridge 91
Wombwell 66

Yarm 9, 23
Yeadon 39
Yearsley 57
York 21, 56, 57, 66, 68,
  86, 104, 107-110, 112,
  114, 118, 120